REVISE EDEXCEL FUNCTIONAL SKILLS ENTRY LEVEL 3

Mathematics

REVISION WORKBOOK

Series Consultant: Harry Smith

Author: Navtej Marwaha

To revise all the topics covered in this book, check out:

Revise Functional Skills Entry Level 3
Mathematics Revision Guide 978 1 292 14568 6

Also in this series:

Revise Functional Skills Level 1
Mathematics Revision Workbook 978 1 292 14562 4

Revise Functional Skills Level 2
Mathematics Revision Workbook 978 1 292 14564 8

THE REVISE SERIES
For the full range of Pearson revision titles, visit:
www.pearsonschools.co.uk/revise

Contents

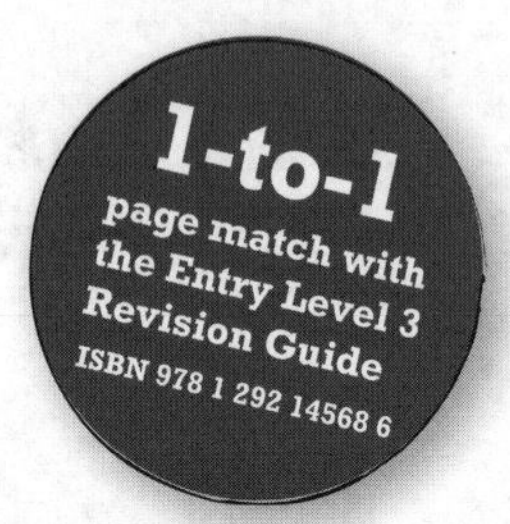

Number

Time

Measures

Shape and space

Handling data

A small bit of small print
Edexcel publishes Sample Test Materials on its website. This is the official content and this book should be used in conjunction with it. The questions in this book have been written to help you practise what you have learned in your revision. Remember: the real test questions may not look like this.

Whole numbers

GUIDED

1 Write these numbers in the place value table.

(a) a three-figure number with a 7 in the hundreds column

(b) a three-figure number with a 5 in the tens column

(c) a two-figure number with a 2 in the units column

hundreds	tens	units
7	1	5

2 Write these numbers in words.

(a) 17 ....

(b) 169 ....

(c) 974 ....

3 Write these numbers in figures.

(a) twenty-eight ....

(b) one hundred and forty-two ....

(c) eight hundred and five ....

4 Write down the value of the digit 5 in each number, in figures.

(a) 53 ....

(b) 598 ....

(c) 957 ....

5 Is the value of the digit 4 smaller in the number 234 or 243? Give a reason for your answer.

....

....

6 This table gives information about the amounts of money four people have in their bank accounts.

Name	Taye	Kayla	Carl	Donald
Amount of money	£982	£992	£980	£995

(a) Who has the most money? ....

(b) Who has the least money? ....

Had a go ☐ Nearly there ☐ Nailed it! ☐

Comparing numbers

GUIDED **1** Which number has the higher value?

(a) 563 or 287 563

(b) 845 or 854 ....

(c) 992 or 993 ....

2 Which number has the lower value?

(a) 673 or 397 ....

(b) 735 or 753 ....

(c) 229 or 228 ....

3 Find the lowest number in each of these lists.

(a) 59, 62, 51, 68, 61 ....

(b) 183, 193, 139, 138, 129 ....

4 Find the highest number in each of these lists.

(a) 78, 72, 73, 63, 75 ....

(b) 543, 445, 521, 475, 529 ....

5 Order these numbers from lowest to highest value.

(a) 96, 114, 89, 98, 124, 210

....

(b) 923, 329, 932, 239, 392

....

6 This table shows information about the number of pupils in each year group at a school.

Year	7	8	9	10	11
Number of pupils	115	93	121	135	132

Which year has:

(a) the greatest number of pupils?

....

(b) between one hundred and twenty and one hundred and twenty-nine pupils?

....

(c) fewer than a hundred pupils?

....

Adding

1 Write down the sign for addition. ....

GUIDED **2** Work out the answers to these calculations.

You can use a calculator to work out the answers.

(a) What is 68 plus 156? 68 + 156 = 224

(b) What is the total of 453 and 284? ....

(c) Work out 568 + 251 ....

3 Add together the numbers in each set.

(a) 34 and 63 ....

(b) 286 and 399 ....

(c) 62, 153 and 269 ....

4 Albert was hosting a party. He bought 112 bottles of cola, 63 bottles of lemonade and 57 bottles of mineral water. How many bottles did he have in total?

....

5 Kiera took five mathematics tests. Her scores were 72 marks, 63 marks, 83 marks, 59 marks and 95 marks. How many marks did she score altogether?

....

6 The distance from Birmingham to Manchester is 86 miles. The distance from Manchester to Aberdeen is 351 miles. Work out the distance from Aberdeen to Birmingham via Manchester.

Remember to give units with your answer.

....

7 This table shows information about the number of pupils in each year group at a school.

Year	7	8	9	10	11
Number of pupils	115	93	121	135	132

Work out the total number of pupils in the school.

....

8 This table gives information about the amounts of money four people have in their bank accounts.

Name	Steve	Jean	Jason	Stephanie
Amount of money	£182	£125	£321	£42

Work out the total amount of money in the four bank accounts.

....

Had a go ☐ Nearly there ☐ Nailed it! ☐

Subtracting

1 Write down the sign for subtraction. ....

GUIDED 2 Work out the answers to these calculations.

(a) Take 63 from 289 289 − 63 = 226

(b) Find the difference between 453 and 284 ....

(c) Work out 568 – 251 ....

3 Work out the answers to these subtractions.

You can use a calculator to work out the answers.

(a) 146 – 54 ....

(b) 596 – 82 ....

(c) 985 – 527 ....

4 43 people were on a bus. 9 people got off at a bus stop and another 15 people got off at the next bus stop. How many people are now on the bus?

....

5 Mr Harris wants to work out how much gas he uses in a week. At the start of the week, the gas meter reading was 569 units. At the end of the week, the gas meter reading was 672 units. How many units of gas has he used in a week?

....

6 The table below shows the cost of three different types of calculator.

Calculator	basic	standard	graphical
Cost	£6	£12	£18

Brenda buys one of each type of calculator. She pays with a £50 note. How much change should she get?

....

7 This table shows some information about the number of pupils in each year group at a school. There are a total of 580 pupils in the school.

Year	7	8	9	10	11
Number of pupils	115	95	125	130	

Work out the number of pupils in Year 11.

....

Multiplication

1 Write down the sign for multiplication. ....

GUIDED **2** Work out the answers to these calculations.

(a) Work out 26 times 7 $26 \times 7 = 182$

(b) Multiply 15 by 8 ....

(c) Work out 24×4 ....

3 Find the answers to these multiplications.

(a) 15×6 ....

(b) 12×10 ....

(c) 32×5 ....

4 A florist sold 25 boxes of flowers. Each box contained 8 flowers.

Work out the total number of flowers sold.

....

5 David buys 15 stamps. Each stamp costs £2. Work out the total cost of the stamps bought.

....

6 Eggs come in three different tray sizes. There are 6 eggs in the small tray. There are twice as many in the medium tray and five times as many in the large tray.

How many eggs are there in:

(a) a medium tray? ....

(b) a large tray? ....

7 Jyoti and Kim are training for a charity run. During each training session, Jyoti does ten 60 metre sprints and Kim runs around the 150 metre track five times.

(a) How far does Jyoti run during each training session?

....

(b) How far does Kim run during each training session?

....

(c) By the time of the charity run, Kim has trained for 6 sessions. How far has she run in total?

....

Had a go ☐ Nearly there ☐ Nailed it! ☐

Division

1 Write down the sign for division. ....

GUIDED 2 Work out the answers to these calculations.

(a) Divide 20 by 4 $20 \div 4 = 5$

(b) Share 70 by 10 ....

(c) How many times does 3 go into 36? ....

(d) How many 10s are there in 150? ....

3 Work out the answers to these divisions.

(a) $45 \div 5$ ....

(b) $300 \div 10$ ....

(c) $144 \div 4$ ....

(d) $234 \div 6$ ....

4 Four people shared a prize draw win of £320 equally. How much does each person receive?

....

5 Sam drives to work and back five days every week. He drives 160 miles in total.
How many miles does Sam drive each day?

....

6 Tim has gone out for dinner with three friends. The meal costs £72. The cost of the meal will be split equally between Tim and his friends. How much will each person pay?

....

7 Ginny packs tins of paint into boxes. Each box holds six paint tins.

(a) How many boxes does she need for 42 tins?

....

(b) How many boxes does she need for 168 tins?

....

8 Norma is going on holiday for six weeks. She takes four tablets each day. How many tablets will she need to take with her in total?

....

Multiplying and dividing by 10, 100 and 1000

GUIDED **1** Work out the answers to these calculations.

(a) A box contains 99 matches. How many matches are there in 10 boxes?

10 × ....

(b) A stationery shop sells packs of A4 card containing 100 sheets each. Tom has 800 sheets of A4 card. How many packs does Tom have?

....

2 Beth measures the width of her cupboard. It measures 2000 mm. She writes this calculation to convert the width of the cupboard door to metres:

width in metres = 2000 ÷ 1000

Calculate the width of the cupboard door in metres.

....

3 Béni wants to book a holiday. He sees this offer.

Top Choice
10 nights in Copenhagen
£67 per person per night including flights and tax

How much will it cost Béni to stay in Copenhagen for 10 nights?

....

4 A kitchen fitter wants to order some materials. This table shows information about the costs.

Item	Cost
washing machine	£120
100 plasterboard sheets	£800
tiles	£8 each

(a) How much do 100 tiles cost?

....

(b) How much does each plasterboard sheet cost?

....

Had a go ☐ Nearly there ☐ Nailed it! ☐

Remainders

GUIDED **1** Work out the remainders for these divisions.

(a) $31 \div 2$ $30 \div 2 = 15$ so the remainder is 1

(b) $54 \div 5$ ....

(c) $252 \div 8$ ....

2 A group of 41 people goes to a restaurant. Each table can seat 5 people.
How many tables does the group need?

....

3 Arif has 19 stamps in one book and 15 stamps in another.
Each parcel needs 3 stamps. How many parcels can Arif post?

Work out the total number of stamps first. Then find the answer by dividing.

....

4 Kevin bought 48 sweets on Monday and 40 sweets on Tuesday. He shared all the sweets between himself and four friends. How many sweets did they each get?

....

5 Kylie has 63 tulips. She needs 12 tulips to make a bunch. How many bunches can she make?

....

6 40 students are going on a trip. At least one teacher must go with every 21 students.
Work out the smallest number of teachers required for the trip.

....

7 Anwar needs 79 cakes for a conference. The cakes come in packs of 4. Anwar thinks he needs 19 packs of cakes. Is he correct? You must show your working.

....

....

8 A teacher has 28 sweets and wants to share them between 5 of her pupils.
She wants to give each pupil the same number of sweets. How many sweets will each pupil receive? How many will she have left over?

....

9 Salvador fills a van with large wooden crates. The weight of each crate is 100 kg. The greatest weight the van can hold is 990 kg. Work out the greatest number of crates that the van can hold.

....

Choosing the right order

1 Crisps cost 35p per packet. A bottle of lemonade costs £1.25. Ravi buys 5 packets of crisps and one bottle of lemonade. He pays with a £10 note. Work out how much change he should get.

5 × 35p = £1.75

£1.75 + £1.25 = ...

£10.00 – £3.00 = ...

2 A builders' merchant buys 25 slabs for £8 each and sells them at £20 each. Work out how much profit the merchant makes.

....

....

3 Mary bought six boxes of chocolates. Each box contained 27 chocolates. Mary ate 36 chocolates herself. She then shared the remaining chocolates among herself and her five friends.

(a) How many chocolates did Mary buy?

....

(b) How many chocolates did each person receive?

....

4 A machine makes 10 bolts every hour. The machine makes bolts for 6 hours each day, 5 days a week.

(a) Work out the total number of bolts made each week.

....

(b) The bolts are packed into boxes. Each box holds 30 bolts. How many boxes are needed for all the bolts made each week?

....

5 A shop sells packets of sweets. There are 12 packets of sweets in each box.
In January, the shop sold all the packets of sweets in 40 boxes. In February, the shop sold all the packets of sweets in 25 boxes.

(a) Work out the total number of packets of sweets the shop sold in January and February.

....

(b) The boxes of sweets are delivered to the shop in vans. A van can carry 30 boxes.
Sandra wants 205 boxes. Work out how many vans are needed to deliver the boxes.

....

Had a go ☐ Nearly there ☐ Nailed it! ☐

Using a calculator

1 Use your calculator to find the answers to these calculations.

(a) $453 + 389$ ....

(b) $672 \div 12$ ....

(c) $652 - 83 - 73 - 159$ ....

(d) $6 + 3 \times 8$ ....

2 Martin wants to buy a new smartphone. In one shop the smartphone costs £242. In another shop the same smartphone costs £281. What is the difference in price?

....

3 The cost of attending the cinema is £8. On Monday, 150 people attend the cinema.

(a) How much do they pay altogether?

....

(b) On Tuesday, the cinema took £2,800 by selling tickets. How many people attended the cinema on Tuesday?

....

4 Alex is paid £1,850 per month after tax. His costs are:

Mortgage	Gas/electricity	Council tax	Telephone	Water	Outgoings
£565	£65	£79	£48	£38	£1,100

Does Alex spend more or less than his monthly income? You must show your working.

....

5 A shop buys 85 chairs for £12 each and sells them at £28 each. Work out how much profit the shop makes.

....

6 Hasan, Norma and their three children went to a theme park. The tickets were £18 for each adult and £15 for each child. What was the total cost of the tickets for Hasan and his family?

....

7 A coffee machine dispenses 20 cups every hour. The coffee machine dispenses for 8 hours each day on 7 days of the week. Work out the total number of cups of coffee dispensed in one week.

....

Multiples

GUIDED **1** Complete this table of multiples.

Number	× 1	× 2	× 3	× 4	× 5	× 6	× 7	× 8	× 9	× 10
2	2	4								
3										
4		8								
5										
6			18							
7										
8						48				
9										
10				40						

2 Look at this list of numbers: 2 3 10 12 15 16 24

From the numbers in the list, write down:

(a) an odd number .... **(b)** a multiple of 6. ....

3 Look at this list of numbers: 5 15 24 40 55 66 90

From the numbers in the list, write down:

(a) two different numbers that add up to an even number ....

(b) a multiple of 4 and 5. ....

4 Look at this list of numbers: 5 6 12 20 25 26 28

From the numbers in the list, write down:

(a) an odd number ....

(b) two numbers that are multiples of 3 ....

(c) two numbers that multiply together to make 30. ....

5 A restaurant needs to seat a group of 20 friends. Each table must have the same number of guests. Each table can seat from 3 to 9 people.

How many people could there be at each table? Give all of the possible answers.

....

Had a go ☐ **Nearly there** ☐ **Nailed it!** ☐

Number patterns

1 Write down the missing terms of these number sequences.

(a) 2, 5, 8, 11, ..., ...

(b) 50, 45, 40, 35, ..., ...

(c) 2, 4, 8, 16, ..., ...

(d) ...., 80, 40, 20, 10, ...

2 Teresa wants to save some money. She has £10 in week 1, £15 in week 2, £20 in week 3, £25 in week 4 and so on. How much does she have in:

(a) week 5? ....

(b) week 6? ....

3 Robert is training for a marathon. He trains every Sunday. On the first Sunday, he runs 5 km. Each Sunday, he increases the length of his run by 2 km. Work how far he runs on:

(a) the 4th Sunday ....

(b) the 9th Sunday ....

4 Arun has bought shares in a company. Their total value is £32 at the end of January. The value increases by 25p each month. What is their total value at the end of April?

....

5 A scientist is growing bacteria. She starts with 25 bacteria. The number of bacteria doubles every hour. How many bacteria will there be after 2 hours?

....

....

6 This calendar shows the days in May 2016. Tara is planning her gym sessions. She starts her gym sessions on Tuesday 3 May. She wants to go to the gym every four days, starting from this date. On which dates in May does Tara need to go to the gym? Circle the dates on the calendar.

May 2016

Mon	Tue	Wed	Thu	Fri	Sat	Sun
						1
2	3	4	5	6	7	8
9	10	11	12	13	14	15
16	17	18	19	20	21	22
23	24	25	26	27	28	29
30	31					

Decimals

GUIDED **1** Which two whole numbers do these numbers lie between?

(a) 14.8 14 and 15

(b) 123.3 ....

(c) 28.78 ....

2 Which whole number is each of these numbers closest to?

(a) 15.7 .... **(b)** 83.3 ....

3 Write down the value of the digit 7 in each of these numbers. Write your answers in words.

(a) 8.76 .... **(b)** 10.67 ....

(c) 73.42 .... **(d)** 7.1 ....

4 Write down the number marked by the arrow.

(a) 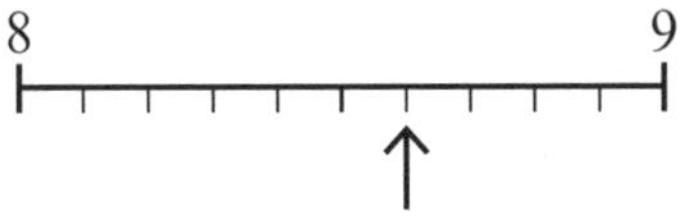 8 — 9 ....

(b) 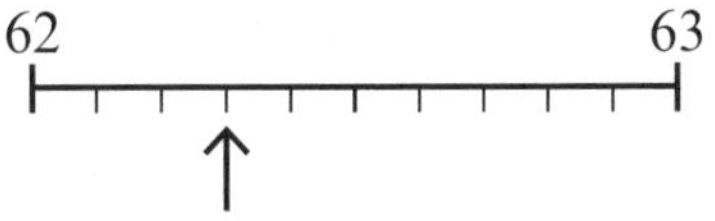 62 — 63 ....

(c) 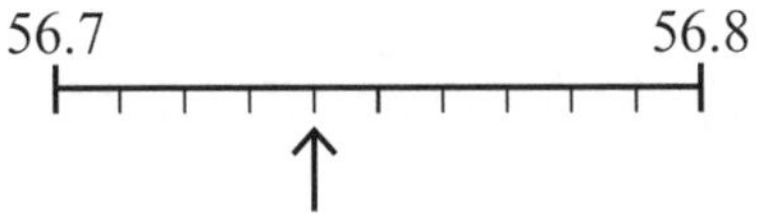 56.7 — 56.8 ....

5 Mark these numbers on the number lines.

(a) 7.6 7 — 8

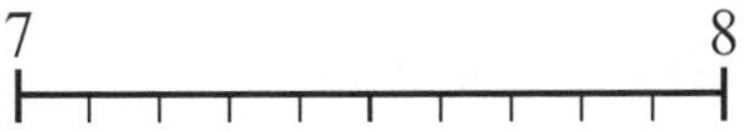

(b) 43.7 43 — 44

6 Write down how many decimal places each number has.

(a) 10.98 .... **(b)** 9.7 ....

(c) 15.08 .... **(d)** 28.30 ....

Had a go ☐ Nearly there ☐ Nailed it! ☐

Ordering decimals

GUIDED **1** Write the larger number in each pair of numbers.

(a) 12.3 and 12.7 12.7

(b) 6.87 and 6.78 ....

(c) 6.04 and 6.40 ....

(d) 8.95 and 8.94 ....

(e) 17.01 and 17.1 ....

(f) 15.2 and 15.20 ....

2 Write these numbers in order of size, starting with the smallest number.

(a) 0.72, 0.81, 0.78 ....

(b) 4.5, 4.23, 3.74 ....

(c) 6.4, 4.6, 6.04 ....

(d) 0.09, 0.8, 0.15 ....

3 This table shows information about the heights, in metres, of three boys.

Name	Ian	James	Seamus
Height (m)	1.63	1.67	1.54

Write the boys' names in order of their heights, starting with the shortest.

....

4 This table shows the fastest lap times, in seconds, of three drivers in a race.

Name	Achatz	Mata	Franklin
Time (s)	90.08	91.04	90.8

Write the list of names in order of lap time, starting with the fastest.

....

5 This table shows the different prices, in £, of a punnet of strawberries at different supermarkets.

Supermarket	A	B	C
Price (£)	2.36	2.34	2.63

Write the list of supermarkets in price order, starting with the most expensive.

....

Fractions

1 What fraction of this shape is shaded?

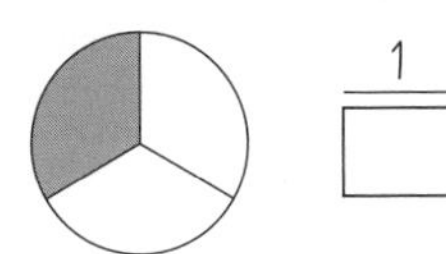

$\frac{1}{\square}$

2 Shade the given fractions of the shapes below.

(a) Shade $\frac{1}{6}$ of this shape. **(b)** Shade $\frac{1}{16}$ of this shape.

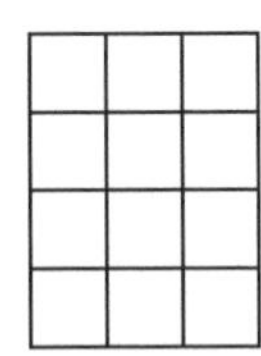

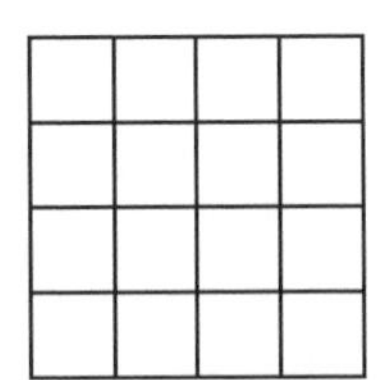

3 What fraction of this shape is not shaded?

....

4 Look at these shapes.

(a) Write down the fraction of this shape that is shaded.

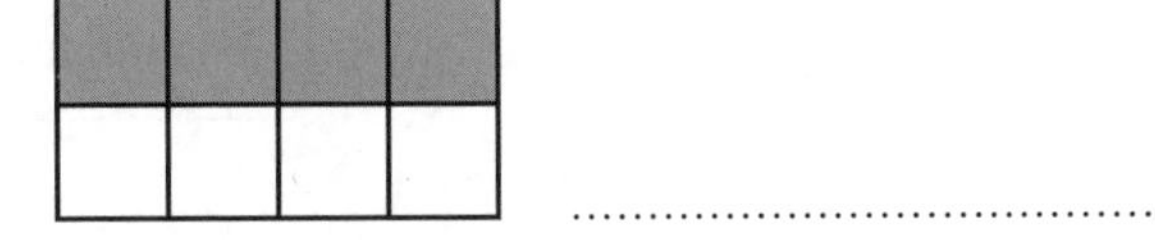

....

(b) Shade $\frac{1}{4}$ of this shape.

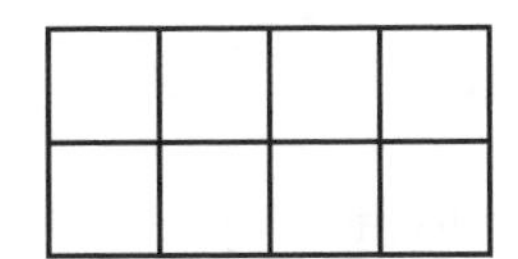

5 Write down these fractions in figures.

(a) a tenth ....

(b) a fifth ....

6 Write down these fractions in words.

(a) $\frac{1}{3}$ ....

(b) $\frac{1}{6}$ ....

7 The diagram shows a scale on a fuel tank. What fraction of the petrol tank is full?

0 $\frac{1}{4}$ $\frac{1}{2}$ $\frac{3}{4}$ Full

....

Had a go ☐ Nearly there ☐ Nailed it! ☐

Types of fractions

GUIDED **1** **(a)** What fraction of this shape is shaded? What fraction is not shaded? Give your answers in figures and words.

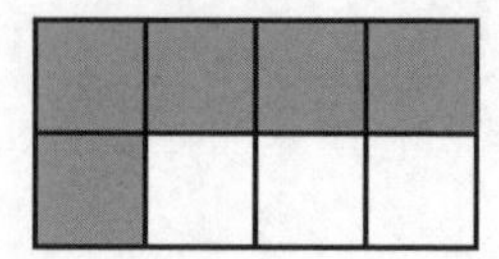

shaded = $\frac{5}{\square}$ five ....

not shaded = ...

(b) Shade $\frac{3}{4}$ of this shape.

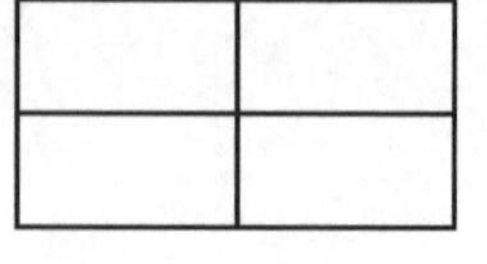

2 What fraction of £8 is £1? Write your answer in figures and words.

....

3 Karen's mark in a mathematics test was 7 out of 10. Write down Karen's mark as a fraction.

....

4 During May, it rained on 14 days. For what fraction of the month did it rain?

> Think about how many days there are in May. This is the denominator of the fraction.

....

5 There are 20 students in a class. 15 of these students are female. What fraction of the class is:

(a) female? .... **(b)** male? ....

6 Shahab bought four jars of mustard. He gave three of them to his brothers.

What fraction of the mustard he bought does he have left?

....

....

7 A guesthouse has single rooms and double rooms. $\frac{2}{5}$ of the rooms are single rooms.

What fraction of the rooms are double rooms?

....

....

Equivalent fractions

1 Is $\frac{5}{10}$ equivalent to $\frac{1}{2}$?

$\frac{1}{2}$ means $1 \div 2$. Use a calculator.

....

2 Circle the two equivalent fractions in each list.

(a) $\frac{3}{4}$ $\frac{1}{2}$ $\frac{3}{6}$

(b) $\frac{4}{4}$ $\frac{2}{4}$ $\frac{2}{2}$

(c) $\frac{1}{4}$ $\frac{2}{5}$ $\frac{2}{8}$

3 For each pair of fractions, decide which is smaller.

(a) $\frac{5}{8}$ or $\frac{1}{2}$? ....

(b) $\frac{2}{5}$ or $\frac{3}{10}$? ....

4 Chiara runs $\frac{3}{4}$ of a lap. Sophie runs $\frac{4}{5}$ of a lap. Have they run the same distance? Give a reason for your answer.

....

....

5 Anna has a pizza. She cuts it into 4 equal slices and eats one of them. Bill has a pizza that is the same size. He cuts it into 8 equal slices and eats two of them.

(a) What fraction of a whole pizza have Anna and Bill each eaten?

Anna ....

Bill ....

(b) Have Anna and Bill eaten the same amount of pizza? Give a reason for your answer.

....

6 Anthony has $\frac{2}{5}$ of a tin of blue paint and $\frac{1}{10}$ of a tin of yellow paint. Anthony needs to mix together equal amounts of blue paint and yellow paint to make green paint. Can he do this by mixing all the blue paint with all the yellow paint? Give a reason for your answer.

....

....

7 Debbie has a job in a factory and a job in a cafe. She also earns some money by selling cakes.

$\frac{2}{3}$ of Debbie's income is from working in the factory. $\frac{1}{4}$ of Debbie's income is from working in the cafe. Does she earn more money in the factory or in the cafe?

....

....

Had a go ☐ **Nearly there** ☐ **Nailed it!** ☐

Fractions of amounts

1 Find these fractions of the given amounts.

$\frac{1}{4}$ of 60 means $60 \div 4$

(a) $\frac{1}{4}$ of 60 ....

(b) $\frac{1}{8}$ of 160 ....

(c) $\frac{1}{3}$ of £96 ....

2 A shop employs 80 people. $\frac{1}{5}$ of them are men.

How many men does the shop employ?

....

GUIDED **3** A worker is paid £240 per week. A third of this is deducted for tax and national insurance.

What amount is deducted for tax and national insurance?

$\frac{1}{3}$ of £240 = 240 ÷ ....

4 A building company is going to build 120 flats. A tenth of the flats have four bedrooms, a quarter of the flats have three bedrooms and the rest of the flats have two bedrooms.

(a) How many flats have four bedrooms?

....

(b) How many flats have three bedrooms?

....

(c) How many flats have two bedrooms?

....

5 Amy earns £2,100 each month. She saves $\frac{1}{5}$ of this.

Brian earns £1,800 each month. He saves $\frac{1}{9}$ of this.
Who saves more money each month?

Don't just write a name. You have to show your working, then write a conclusion.

....

....

Rounding whole numbers

1 Round these numbers to the nearest ten.

(a) 8 ....
(b) 23 ....

(c) 59 ....
(d) 198 ....

2 Round these numbers to the nearest hundred.

(a) 82 ....
(b) 123 ....

(c) 268 ....
(d) 675 ....

3 A bike ride takes 87 minutes. How many minutes is this, to the nearest 10?

....

4 A shop sold 64 magazines in a week. How many magazines did it sell, to the nearest 10?

....

5 There are 245 pens in a pot. How many pens are there, rounded to the nearest 100?

....

6 Simon and Peter are playing a game. They each pick a card with a number written on it. They each round their number to the nearest 10. If it rounds up, they get two points. If it rounds down, they get no points.

Simon picks number 59. How many points does he get? ....

Peter picks number 72. How many points does he get? ....

7 The manager of a theatre is talking about how many people watched a play. There were 90 men to the nearest ten, and 60 women to the nearest ten.

What is the smallest number that rounds up to 90? What is the smallest number that rounds up to 60?

The manager says that at least 150 people attended the play. Show that this may not be true.

....

....

Had a go ☐ Nearly there ☐ Nailed it! ☐

Rounding money

GUIDED **1** Round these numbers to the nearest whole number.

(a) 8.3 8 **(b)** 17.42 .... **(c)** 38.69 ....

2 Round these amounts to the nearest pound.

(a) £5.29 .... **(b)** £24.79 .... **(c)** £96.08 ....

GUIDED **3** Round these prices to the nearest pound.

(a) A bike that costs £57.51 costs £58 to the nearest pound.

(b) A door that costs £123.48 costs .... to the nearest pound.

(c) A sofa that costs £653.50 costs .... to the nearest pound.

(d) A car that costs £984.75 costs .... to the nearest pound.

4 This table gives the prices of some items sold in a supermarket.

Bananas	Cereal	Steaks	Juice	Pizza	Lamb chops
£1.65	£4.25	£8.59	£2.99	£6.75	£8.15

(a) Alan wants to buy bananas and lamb chops. He has £10 to spend. Round the amounts to the nearest pound to estimate whether Alan has enough money.

....

(b) Bella wants to buy steaks, juice and pizza. She has £15 to spend. Round the amounts to the nearest pound to estimate whether Bella has enough money.

....

(c) Taz wants to buy bananas, cereal, steaks, juice, pizza and lamb chops. He has £35 to spend. Round the amounts to the nearest pound to estimate whether Taz has enough money.

....

Estimating

1 Estimate the answers to these calculations.

(a) $93 + 48 \approx$ $90 + 50 \approx$ ....

(b) $937 - 82 \approx$ ....

(c) $84 \times 9 \approx$ ....

(d) $37 \div 4 \approx$ ....

2 Isolde went shopping for some new clothes. She bought a blouse for £49.99 and a coat for £93.45. Estimate how much she spent.

....

3 Torsten wants to buy some ribbon that costs £4.20 per metre.

Estimate how much he will pay for 29 metres of ribbon.

....

4 A farmer bought 479 kg of fertiliser at a cost of £19 per kilogram.

Estimate the total cost of the fertiliser.

....

5 A litre of detergent will clean 24 m^2 of patio.

Estimate how many 1 litre cans are needed to clean a patio area of 123 m^2.

....

6 Pam sold 48 radiators for £89 each. They cost her £32 each.

Estimate how much profit she made.

....

7 A small coin weighs 2 g.

(a) Estimate the weight of 190 coins.

....

(b) Estimate the number of coins in a bag that weighs 889 g.

....

Had a go ☐ Nearly there ☐ Nailed it! ☐

Checking your answer

GUIDED **1** Use estimation to check whether these statements are likely to be correct.

> If the number is between 10 and 99, round to the nearest 10
> If the number is between 100 and 999, round to the nearest 100

(a) $68 + 93 = 161$

70 + 90 = 160 so the answer 161 is likely to be correct as it is close to 160

(b) $409 - 64 = 345$

....

(c) $672 + 543 - 283 = 932$

....

GUIDED **2** Check by using inverse operations whether the following statements are correct. For any that are incorrect, write down the correct answers.

(a) $600 - 319 = 281$

281 + 319 = 600, so it is correct.

(b) $550 + 254 = 804$

....

(c) $48 \times 6 = 288$

....

(d) $848 \div 8 = 206$

....

3 Alice worked out that the answer to 21×9 is 69. Use estimation to decide whether she is likely to be correct.

....

4 Kate and four of her friends go to a restaurant. The bill comes to £64.00. The bill is shared equally by Kate and her four friends.

(a) Work out how much each person pays.

....

(b) Use estimation or inverse operations to check your answer.

....

Problem-solving practice

1 Rohan wants to buy a camera. The salesperson says Rohan can choose one of these deals.

Deal A	**Deal B**
Pay £895 today	Pay £50 per month for 18 months

Which deal is cheaper? Check your answer.

....

....

2 Robert wants to buy some concrete posts. He finds two companies on the internet.

Cheap Posts	**FenceWorld**
Posts usually £15 each	Posts usually £8 each
Buy today, pay $\frac{1}{3}$ of the usual price.	Buy today, pay $\frac{1}{2}$ of the usual price.

Robert wants to pay as little as possible. Which of the two shops should Robert buy the concrete posts from?

Remember to show all your working and write a conclusion.

....

....

....

3 Manfred is going to replace the curtains in his room. He needs 5 metres of fabric. He also needs a packet of curtain rings. Here are the prices.

Fabric per metre	£8
Packet of curtain rings	£2.50

He pays with three £20 notes. How much change does he get?

....

4 A haulage company wants to deliver crates of fruit. The company has 259 crates to deliver. 102 are sent by train and the rest will go by lorries.

(a) How many crates will be delivered by lorry?

....

(b) A lorry can take only 15 crates. How many lorries are needed to deliver the crates?

....

Had a go ☐ **Nearly there** ☐ **Nailed it!** ☐

Problem-solving practice

1 Nikolaas sells mortgages for a bank. Every month, Nikolaas doubles the number of mortgages he sold the month before. In January, he sold six mortgages.

Complete the table to show how many mortgages Nikolaas sells each month.

Month	Jan	Feb	Mar	Apr
Number of mortgages	6			

2 Ronald wants to buy some gifts for his family. This table shows the prices of some items in a shop.

Item	Price
aftershave	£14.56
perfume	£11.15
purse	£18.78
lipstick	£8.25
watch	£23.99

Ronald decides to buy some perfume, a purse and a watch.

(a) Work out an estimate for the cost of Ronald's shopping.

....

(b) Ronald pays with three £20 notes. Work out an estimate for the change he receives.

....

3 Maz is trying to complete sudoku puzzles in less than 15 minutes.
Here are three of his times, in minutes: 14.63 14.36 14.56

Order Maz's times from shortest to longest.

....

Calendars

1 Andrew ordered a computer on Wednesday 23 March 2016. He was told that the computer would be delivered on the Friday of the next week. What date was the computer delivered?

....

....

....

2 The calendar shows the days in September 2016. Starting from Tuesday 6 September, write down the number of days until the following appointments.

(a) doctor's on 15 September

....

(b) bank manager on 26 September

....

(c) parents' evening on 30 September

....

September 2016

Mon	Tue	Wed	Thu	Fri	Sat	Sun
			1	2	3	4
5	6	7	8	9	10	11
12	13	14	15	16	17	18
19	20	21	22	23	24	25
26	27	28	29	30		

3 The calendars show the days in October and November 2016.

October 2016

Mon	Tue	Wed	Thu	Fri	Sat	Sun
					1	2
3	4	5	6	7	8	9
10	11	12	13	14	15	16
17	18	19	20	21	22	23
24	25	26	27	28	29	30
31						

November 2016

Mon	Tue	Wed	Thu	Fri	Sat	Sun
	1	2	3	4	5	6
7	8	9	10	11	12	13
14	15	16	17	18	19	20
21	22	23	24	25	26	27
28	29	30				

(a) How many days are there from Wednesday 19 October to Wednesday 16 November?

....

(b) Karen books a flight on Thursday 20 October and her return flight is 17 days later. Write down the date she flies back.

....

Had a go ☐ **Nearly there** ☐ **Nailed it!** ☐

Units of time

1 Write numbers to complete the sentences.

(a) There are .... minutes in an hour.

(b) There are .... days in a week.

(c) There are .... seconds in a minute.

GUIDED **2** Write each amount of time in seconds.

(a) 2 minutes $2 \times 60 = 120$ seconds

(b) 3 minutes $3 \times 60 =$ ....

(c) 4 minutes ....

3 Convert these times to minutes.

(a) a quarter of an hour ....

(b) three quarters of an hour ....

(c) 2 hours ....

4 Imani goes to the bank. It takes her $\frac{1}{2}$ an hour to walk to the bank. She spends $\frac{1}{4}$ of an hour at the bank. It then takes her $\frac{1}{2}$ an hour to walk back home.

How long does the whole trip take?

....

....

5 Karim trains in a gym during the day. He does the following exercises.

Exercise	running	rowing	cross-training
Time spent on exercise	45 minutes	30 minutes	1 hour 15 minutes

What is the total amount of time Karim spent on the exercises?

....

6 Zach records two TV programmes. The first lasts 1 hour 30 minutes, and the second lasts 2 hours 45 minutes. How long are his recordings in total?

....

7 Arun is travelling from his house to Leeds. It takes him half an hour to get to the coach station. He waits $\frac{1}{4}$ of an hour for the coach. The coach journey takes 60 minutes.

How long does the journey take in total?

....

12-hour clock

GUIDED **1** Complete these sentences.

(a) 15 minutes is a quarter of an hour.

(b) 30 minutes is .... of an hour.

(c) 45 minutes is .... of an hour.

2 Write the times shown on these analogue clocks, using 12-hour time.

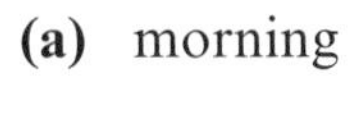

(a) morning ....

(b) afternoon ....

(c) evening ....

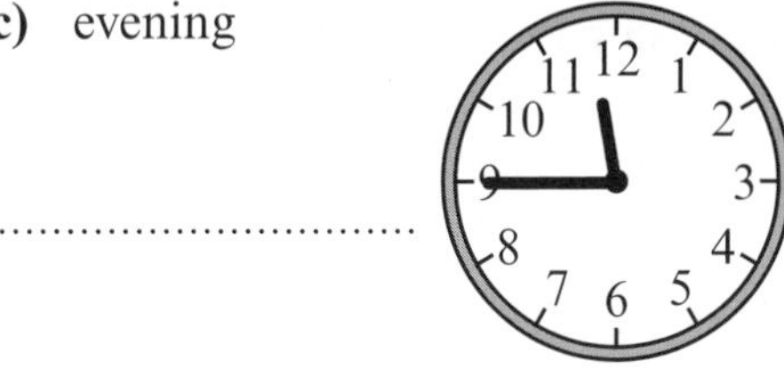

(d) morning ....

3 Draw hands on each clock for the time given.

(a) 9.30 a.m.

(b) 6.15 p.m.

4 Write each time, using the 12-hour clock.

(a) quarter past two in the morning ....

(b) half past five in the evening ....

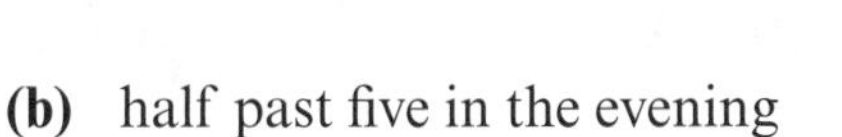

(c) three o'clock in the afternoon ....

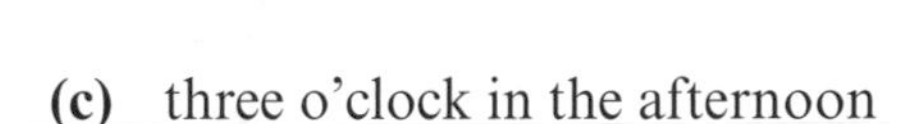

(d) quarter to eight in the morning ....

(e) ten to one in the afternoon ....

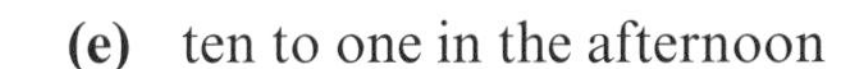

GUIDED **5** Match each digital clock with an analogue clock that shows the same time.

Had a go ☐ Nearly there ☐ Nailed it! ☐

24-hour clock

GUIDED **1** Convert these times to 24-hour times:

(a) 10.30 a.m. 10:30

(b) 2.25 p.m. ....

(c) 4.28 p.m. ....

(d) 5.15 a.m. ....

(e) 5 minutes past midnight ....

(f) 12.15 p.m. ....

GUIDED **2** Convert these 24-hour times to 12-hour times.

(a) 08:32 8.32 a.m.

(b) 1:16 ....

(c) 20:35 ....

(d) 18:42 ....

(e) 11:45 ....

(f) 16:30 ....

3 Write the times shown on these analogue clocks using the 24-hour clock.

(a) morning

....

(b) afternoon

....

(c) evening

....

(d) evening

....

4 Draw hands on each clock for the time given.

(a) 23:30

(b) 07:15

5 Write these times using the 24-hour clock.

(a) quarter to eight in the morning ....

(b) ten to one in the afternoon ....

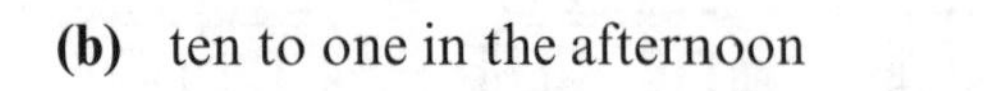

(c) twenty past seven in the morning ....

Time calculations

1 Write down the amount of time between:

(a) 10.30 a.m. and 12.45 p.m. ....

(b) 15:30 and 19:15 ....

(c) 20:45 and 23:15 ....

2 Alison and Bhavnisha meet in London one afternoon.

(a) Alison sets off from home at 2.30 p.m. The journey takes 2 hours and 30 minutes. At what time does she arrive?

....

(b) Bhavnisha travels for 1 hour and 45 minutes. She arrives in London at 5.45 p.m. What time did she set off?

....

3 Herbert and Mike decide to renovate their flat.

(a) Mike thinks that laying the carpet will take 3 hours and 30 minutes. He begins at 15:30. What time does he expect to finish?

....

(b) Herbert needs to finish painting the bathroom by 13:15. The painting will take 2 hours and 45 minutes. What is the latest time he can start?

....

4 Julie joined the queue at the cinema to buy snacks at twenty to eight in the evening. She bought popcorn and a bottle of cola. She sat down with her friends in the cinema at eight o'clock in the evening.

(a) How long did it take Julie to buy the snacks and get back to her seat?

....

(b) The film started at 20:15. The film lasted one hour and thirty minutes. At what time did the film finish?

....

5 Mike sets off from Shrewsbury at 13:30 to go to Kidderminster. The journey takes 1 hour and 20 minutes. What time does Mike arrive in Kidderminster?

....

Had a go ☐ Nearly there ☐ Nailed it! ☐

Timetables

1 Here is part of a timetable for a bus from Wolverhampton to Wombourne.

Wolverhampton	05:50	06:30	07:00	07:40
Penn	06:00	06:40	07:10	08:00
Wombourne	06:10	06:50	07:20	08:05

(a) Mary takes the 05:50 bus from Wolverhampton. What time does she arrive in Penn?

....

(b) Mary takes the 07:40 bus from Wolverhampton.

How long does the journey take to Wombourne?

....

2 The following timetable is for the sleeper train from Fort William to London.
It sets off from Fort William in the evening and arrives in London the next morning.

(a) On which day is the longest journey?

....

	Mon–Fri	**Sun**
Fort William	19:50	19:00
London	07:50	07:50

(b) How long is the shortest journey?

....

3 Here is part of a train timetable from Birmingham to York.

(a) Michelle catches the 08:15 train from Birmingham. How long will it take to get to York?

Birmingham	08:15	08:45	09:00
York	09:50	10:20	10:35

....

(b) Naresh has a meeting in York. He has to be in York before 10:25.

Write down the departure time of the latest train that he can catch.

....

4 This is part of a train timetable from Bleasby to Grimsby.

Bleasby	11:30	12:00	12:30	13:00
Grimsby	12:45	13:15	13:45	14:15

(a) How long does it take to get from Bleasby to Grimsby?

....

(b) A train leaves Bleasby at 14:00. At what time should it arrive in Grimsby?

....

Problem-solving practice

GUIDED **1** Sanjay is cycling into town. He leaves at 14:30. It takes him 30 minutes. He spends 1 hour 15 minutes having lunch in town. He spends 45 minutes cycling back home.

(a) What time does Sanjay have his lunch? Write your answer using the 24-hour clock.

14:30 + 30 mins = ...

(b) What time does Sanjay arrive back home? Write your answer using the 24-hour clock.

....

2 Philip is staying overnight in a hotel. He has a wake-up call booked for 5.30 a.m. He goes to sleep at 10.30 p.m. How long can he sleep for before he is woken up?

....

3 The table shows the amount of time it takes for some services to be completed by a mobile hairdresser.

Service	Time taken
haircut	45 minutes
shave	15 minutes
hair removal	1 hour 15 minutes
manicure	30 minutes

How long do these services take in total? Give your answer in hours and minutes.

....

4 The calendar shows the days in December 2016. The shaded days show the days that a bank is closed.

(a) Anjali puts a cheque into her bank account on 9 December. It takes 4 working days to clear. What date does her cheque clear?

....

....

(b) Ravina orders a new chequebook on 6 December. The chequebook will be delivered in 14 working days. What date should she receive the chequebook?

....

Had a go ☐ Nearly there ☐ Nailed it! ☐

Problem-solving practice

1 Candice wanted to book a room at the Premier Hotel. She enquired about the hotel room on Tuesday 8 March 2016. The hotel told Candice that an en-suite room was available on the Thursday of the next week. What date was the en-suite room available?

....

2 Rodney is a student. On Mondays, he has to attend four lectures at these times:

Ethics 15:30 Philosophy 11.00 a.m. Politics 12.45 p.m. Logic 16:45

(a) Write down the time for Ethics using the 12-hour clock. ....

(b) Write down the time for Politics using the 24-hour clock. ....

(c) List the four lectures in the correct time order.

....

GUIDED 3 Here is part of an incomplete train timetable from London to Swansea.

London	1105	1205	1305
Swansea	1405	1455	....

Jasmine gets to the station in London at 10:45. She waits for the next train to Swansea.

(a) How long does she have to wait?

11:05 – 10:45 = ...

(b) At what time should she arrive at Swansea?

....

(c) Karen gets the 12:05 train from London. How long does the journey take to Swansea?

....

(d) Lorna gets the 13:05 train from London. It takes 2 hours 45 minutes. What time does she arrive in Swansea?

....

4 Andrew wants to go to the cinema to see a film.

The film starts at 7.25 p.m. The film is 2 hours and 20 minutes long. Andrew knows that the last bus home goes at 9.50 p.m. Can Andrew watch the whole film and catch the last bus?

....

Had a go ☐ Nearly there ☐ Nailed it! ☐

Units

GUIDED **1** Draw lines to match the words with the correct descriptions.

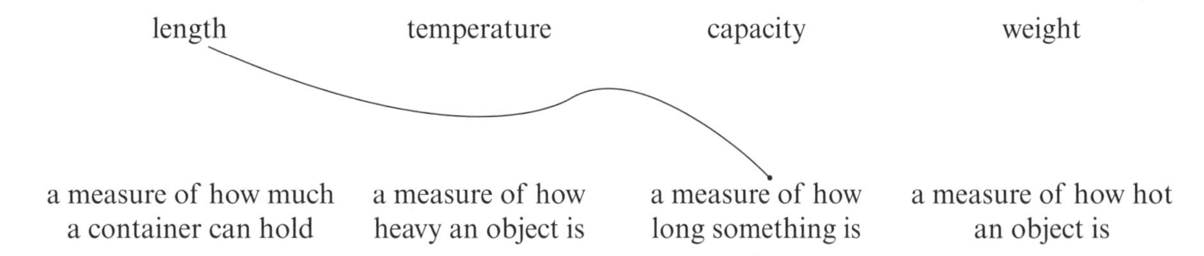

length | temperature | capacity | weight

a measure of how much a container can hold | a measure of how heavy an object is | a measure of how long something is | a measure of how hot an object is

GUIDED **2** Write these units in the correct columns of the table below.

centimetres	grams	inches	Fahrenheit
tonnes	millilitres	~~pints~~	Celsius

Weight	Distance	Capacity	Temperature
		pints	

3 Write these units in the correct rows of the table below.

miles	centimetres	pints	pounds	kilograms	litres

Imperial	
Metric	

4 Read the list of units. Write each unit under the type of device you might use to measure it.

Celsius	centimetres	litres	kilograms
pints	pounds	Fahrenheit	inches

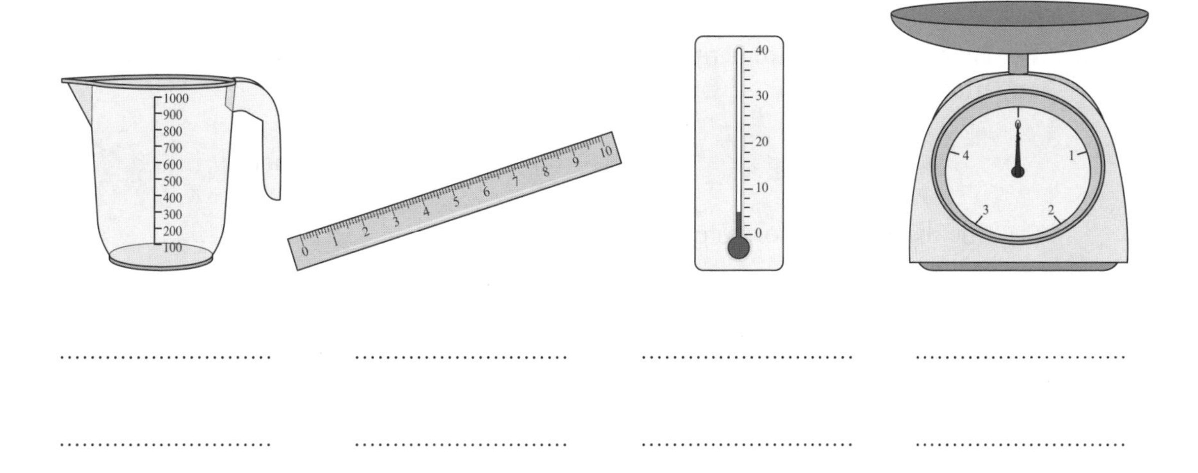

Had a go ☐ Nearly there ☐ Nailed it! ☐

Length

GUIDED **1** Write numbers to complete the sentences.

You need to remember these metric conversions.

(a) There are 10 millimetres in 1 centimetre.

(b) There are .... centimetres in 1 metre.

(c) There are .... metres in 1 kilometre.

2 Convert these measures to the units given.

(a) 3 cm to mm ....

(b) 2 m to cm ....

(c) 7 km to m ....

3 Order these lengths from shortest to longest:

(a) 70 mm 70 cm 7 m ....

(b) 40 km 50 cm 40 m ....

4 Find the total of these lengths. Give your answers in centimetres.

(a) 340 cm, 4 m ....

(b) 50 cm and 2 m ....

5 Rajesh wants to go on the rollercoaster. He sees this sign.

> **Attention**
>
> To go on the rollercoaster, you must be at least 125 cm tall.

Rajesh is 1.35 metres tall. Can Rajesh go on the rollercoaster?

....

6 For each of the measurements below, write an appropriate metric unit and an appropriate imperial unit.

	metric	imperial
(a) the distance of Worcester from Edinburgh	....	....
(b) the height of a tree	....	....

Measuring lengths

1 Use a ruler to measure the lengths of these lines and write down their lengths in millimetres.

(a) ______________ length = ...

(b) ___________________________ length = ...

(c) ______________________ length = ...

(d) ____ length = ...

2 In the space below, draw straight lines with the following lengths.

(a) 36 mm

(b) 4.5 cm

(c) 7 cm

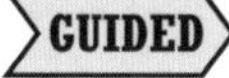

3 Harry saw this picture of two dinosaurs in a book. The diagrams have been drawn to the same scale. The large dinosaur was 26 m long in real life. Estimate the length of the small dinosaur.

The small dinosaur is about half as long as the large dinosaur, so ....

....

....

4 The picture of a car and a lorry have been drawn accurately to the same scale. The real length of the car is 3 m. Estimate the real length of the lorry.

Use a ruler to measure the drawings of the car and the lorry first.

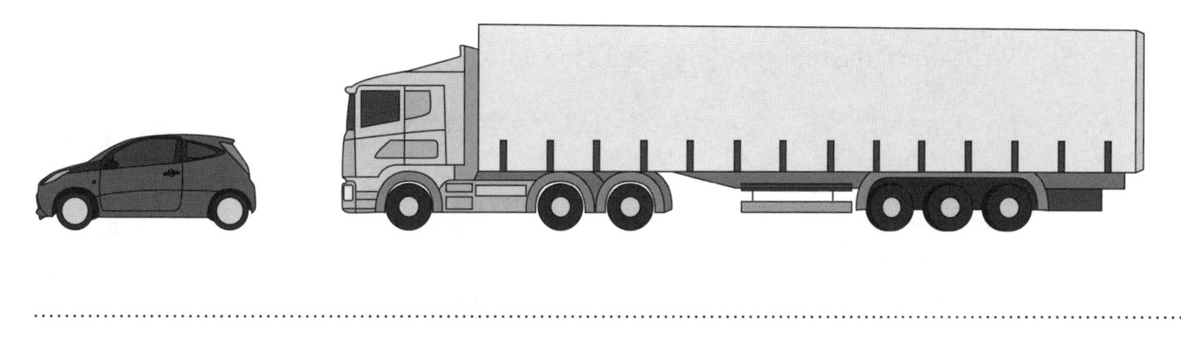

....

....

Had a go ☐ Nearly there ☐ Nailed it! ☐

Reading scales

1 Write down the number marked with an arrow.

(a) 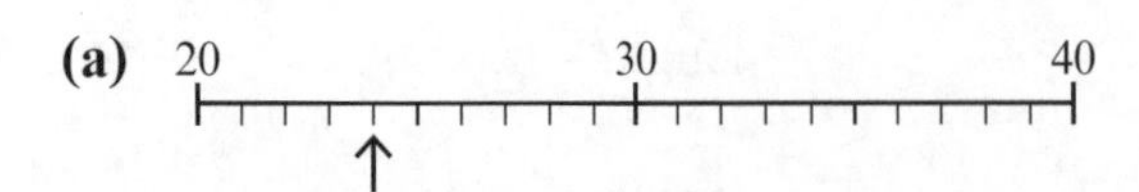

....

(b) 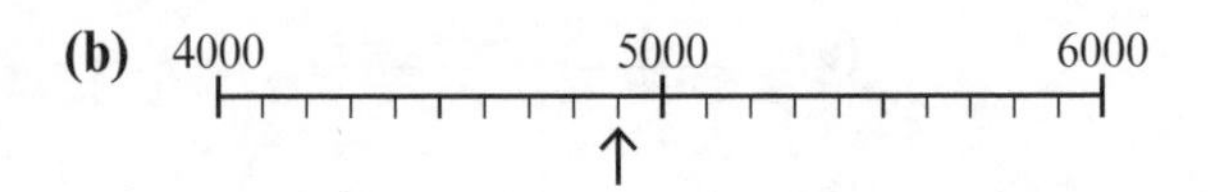

....

2 Find these numbers on the number lines. Mark them with arrows.

(a) 36 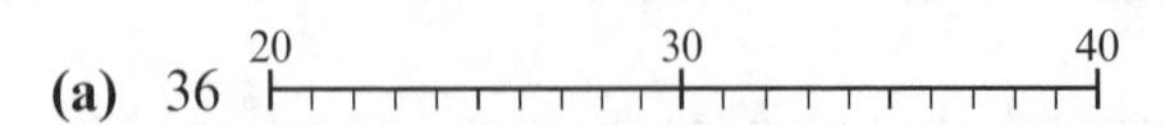

(b) 280 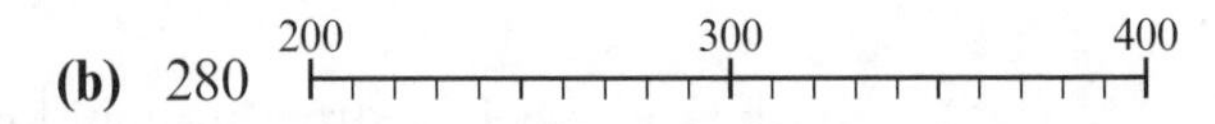

3 Look at these measuring beakers.

(a) How much liquid is in this beaker?

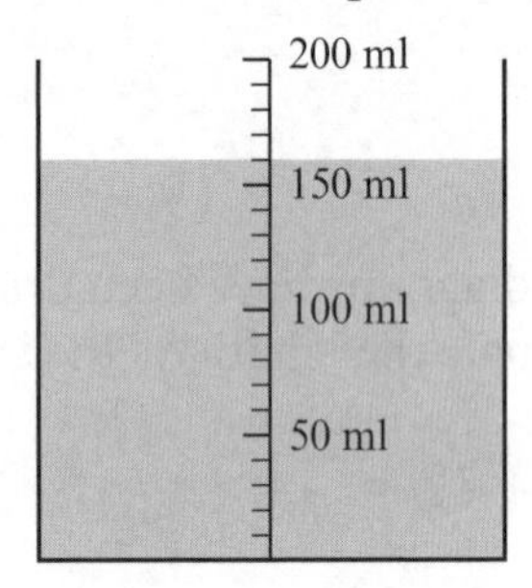

....

(b) Shade this beaker to show 140 ml.

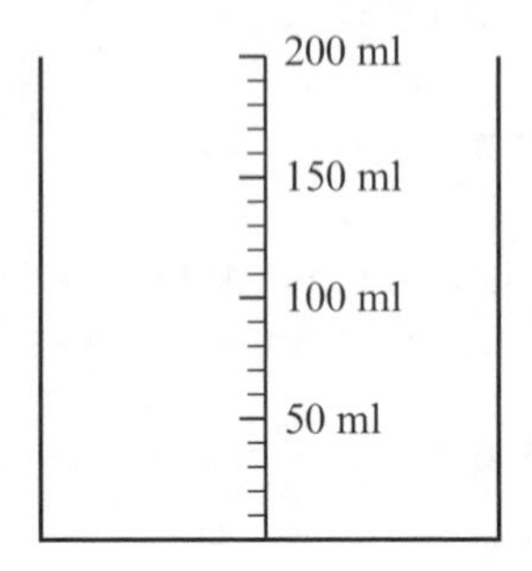

4 Look at these speedometers.

(a) Write down the speed shown by this speedometer.

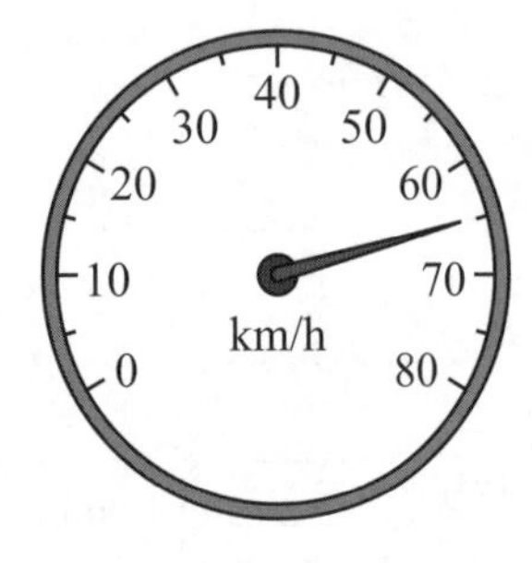

....

(b) Mark 55 km/h on this speedometer with an arrow.

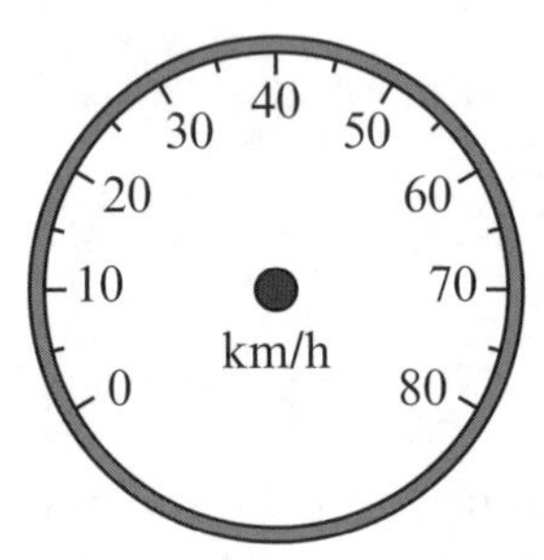

5 Write down the scale readings. State the units.

(a) 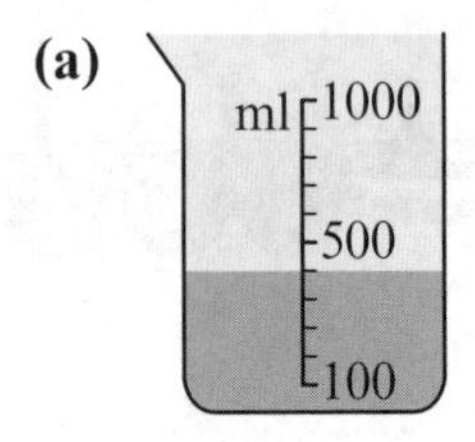

....

(b) 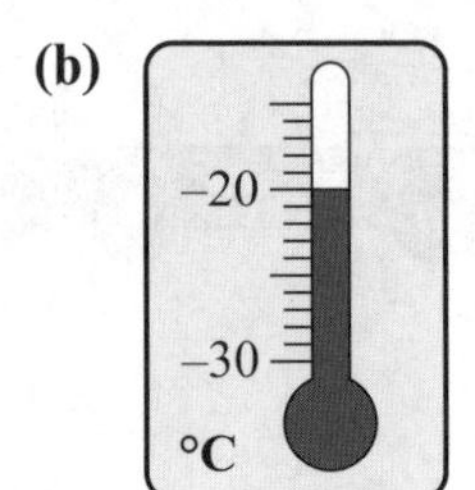

....

(c) 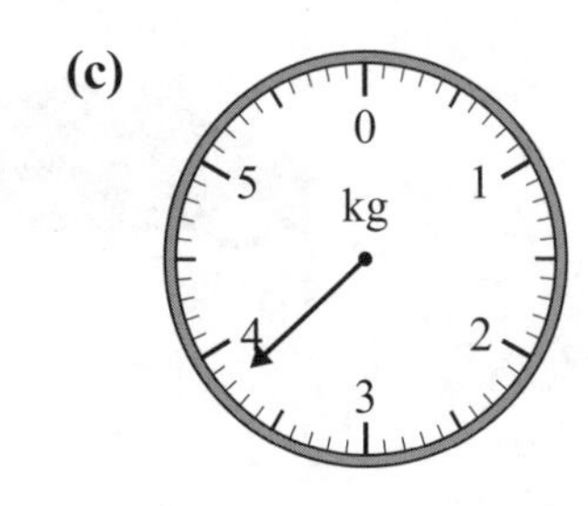

....

Temperature

1 Here are five recorded temperatures: 23 °C 14 °C 19 °C 29 °C 17 °C

(a) Write down the lowest temperature. ....

(b) Write down the highest temperature. ....

(c) Find the difference between the highest and the lowest temperatures.

....

2 Adrian wants to go on holiday to a different country. He wants to go in August.
He finds the average August temperature of some countries. Here are his results.

Country	India	Spain	China	South Africa	Brazil
Temperature (°F)	82	75	81	77	78

(a) Write down the name of the country with the lowest temperature.

....

(b) Write down the name of the country with the highest temperature.

....

(c) Find the difference between the lowest and highest temperatures.

....

3 Look at these thermometers.

(a) What temperature does this thermometer show?

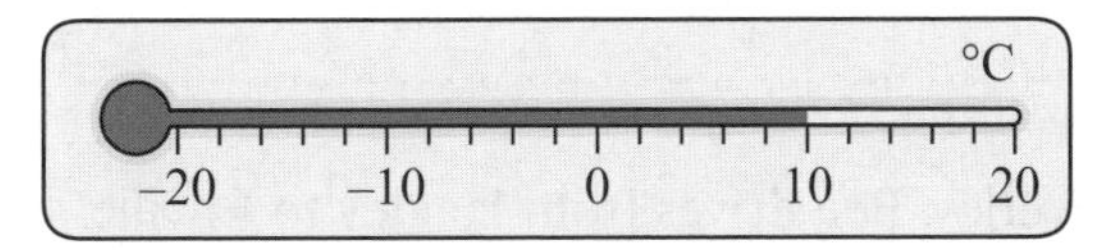

....

(b) Shade this thermometer to show 16 °C.

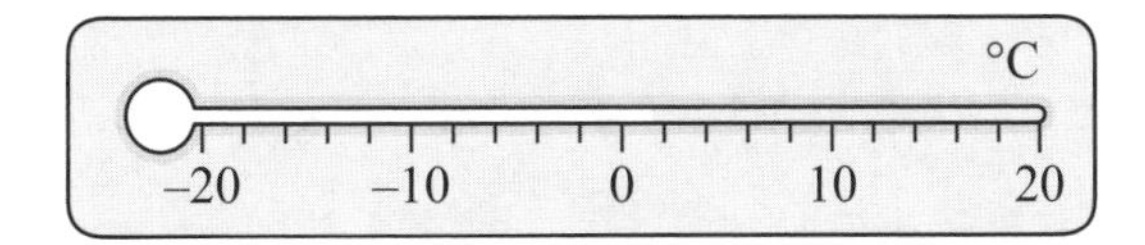

4 Nancy wrote down the temperature at different times on 1 July 2016. Here are the results.

Time	9.00 a.m.	midday	3.00 p.m.	6.00 p.m.	9.00 p.m.
Temperature	19 °C	24 °C	23 °C	21 °C	17 °C

Work out the difference in the temperatures at 3.00 p.m. and 6.00 p.m.

....

Had a go ☐ Nearly there ☐ Nailed it! ☐

Distances

GUIDED **1** Write a unit that could be used for each measurement.

	Imperial	Metric
the distance between two towns	miles	
the distance around a small garden		
the length of the River Thames		

2 Tom is a travelling salesperson. He records how far he travels for work each week. By Wednesday morning, he has already travelled 688 miles. By Wednesday evening, he has travelled 983 miles in total.

Work out how far Tom travels on Wednesday.

....

3 Curtis rides his bike to work and back each day. The distance from his house to his office is 9 km.

(a) Work out the total distance Curtis rides his bike each day.

....

(b) Curtis works from Monday to Friday. Work out the total distance Curtis rides his bike over the week.

....

4 This diagram shows the distances between four villages.

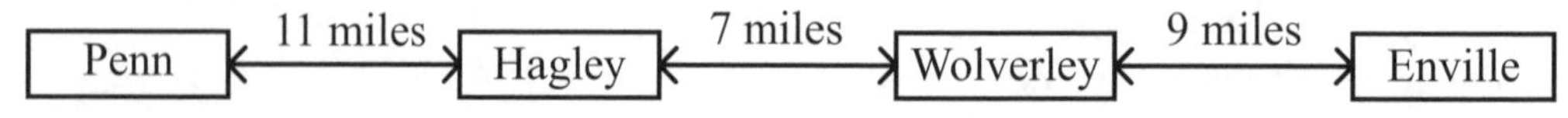

(a) Work out the distance from Penn to Wolverley.

....

(b) Amy drives from Penn to Wolverley. Ben drives from Hagley to Enville. Who drives further?

....

....

5 This diagram shows a park in the shape of a triangle. The length of each side is given.

Olu walks the full distance around the edge of the park. How far does he walk?

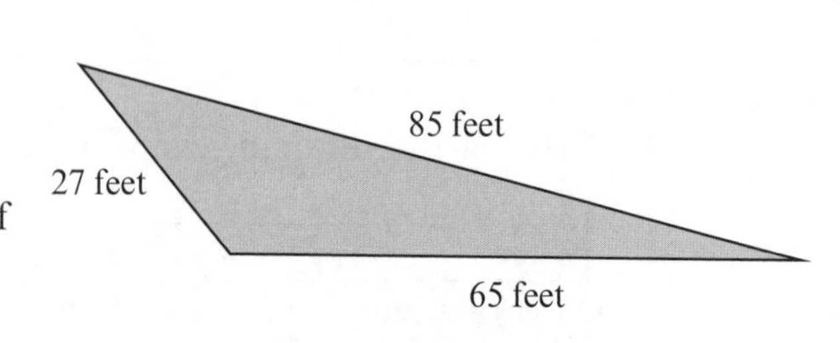

....

Routes

1 This diagram shows the distances between four areas in a nature reserve.

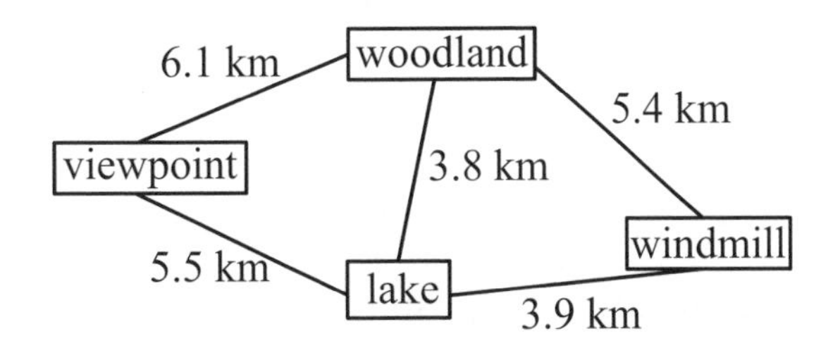

(a) What is the distance between the woodland and the windmill? ....

(b) Which attraction is 5.5 km from the lake? ....

(c) What is the shortest route from the viewpoint to the windmill?

....

(d) Gedi is planning a long-distance race. It must begin and end at the lake. The route must be between 13 and 14 kilometres long in total. Suggest a suitable route.

....

....

2 This diagram shows the distances in miles between locations Anjali visits for work.

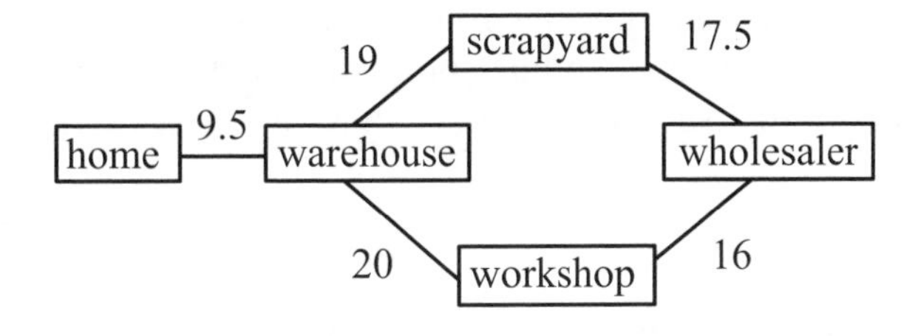

(a) How many miles is it from the warehouse to the workshop?

....

(b) Anjali is at home. She needs to visit the wholesaler. What is the quickest route?

....

(c) Anjali is at the scrapyard. She needs to visit the warehouse and the workshop and then go home. What is the quickest route?

....

....

Had a go ☐ Nearly there ☐ Nailed it! ☐

Weight

1 Choose one word from this list to fill in each gap in these sentences.
kilograms, pounds, grams, stones, tonnes

(a) .... and .... are metric units.

(b) .... and .... are imperial units.

2 Write a sensible unit for each measurement. You could choose a metric unit or an imperial unit.

(a) The weight of a man ....

(b) The weight of lorry ....

(c) The weight of a grape ....

3 Which weight is larger, 50 kg or 50 g? ....

4 Order these weights from smallest to largest: 7 tonnes, 700 grams, 7 kilograms

....

5 Dean wants to lose some weight. He weighs 168 pounds when he starts. He diets for 6 months. At the end of his diet, he weighs 134 pounds. Work out how much weight Dean loses.

....

6 Tamara is going on holiday. She fills her suitcase with some clothes and some books. Her clothes weigh 11.5 kg and her books weigh 4.5 kg. Her suitcase weighs 0.5 kg. If the suitcase weighs more than 15 kg in total, she will have to pay extra. Does Tamara have to pay extra?

....

7 A bag of potatoes weighs 30 kg. Richard's van can only carry a weight of 500 kg. He needs to deliver 18 bags of potatoes to the warehouse.

Can Richard deliver the bags of potatoes in one journey?

....

8 Alan, Ben and Carl are on a rowing team. Alan weighs 68 kg, Ben weighs 72 kg, and Carl weighs 65 kg. They need a fourth person for their team. The total weight of the team cannot exceed 280 kg.

Here is a list of people they can ask to join the team: Don (77 kg) Eric (71 kg) Farah (76 kg)

Who should be the fourth member of the team?

....

Weight calculations

1 Write a number to complete the sentence.

There are .... grams in 1 kilogram.

2 Convert these measures to the units given.

(a) 6 kg to grams

....

(b) 8 kg to grams

....

3 Find the total of these weights, in grams.

Convert all of the weights to the same units first.

(a) 4500 g and 200 g ....

(b) 2 kg and 850 g ....

(c) $\frac{1}{2}$ kg and 400 g ....

4 Which weight is smaller, 3400 g or 3.5 kg?

....

5 Poppy needs 200 g of clay to make one ornament.
How many clay ornaments can she make from a slab of clay weighing 8 kg?

Convert 8 kg into grams.

....

6 Henry is sending a package. The courier will only deliver packages that weigh 5 kg or less.
He puts three parcels into the one package. The parcels weigh 2.5 kg, 2200 g and 900 g.

Will the package be more than the maximum weight?

....

7 Karen is baking for a cake sale. Each tray of cupcakes requires 140 g of flour. She has 1 kg of flour.

Does she have enough flour to make nine trays of cupcakes?

....

Had a go ☐ **Nearly there** ☐ **Nailed it!** ☐

Capacity

GUIDED **1** Fill in the gaps in these sentences.

(a) C .... is a measure of how much something can hold.

(b) V .... is a measure of the amount of space something takes up.

2 This diagram shows a measuring jug containing some water.

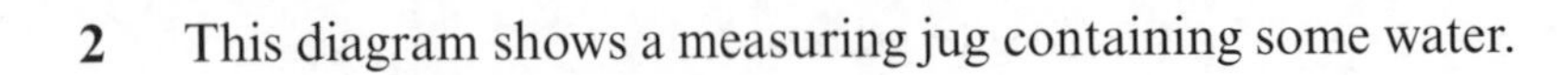

(a) What is the capacity of this measuring jug?

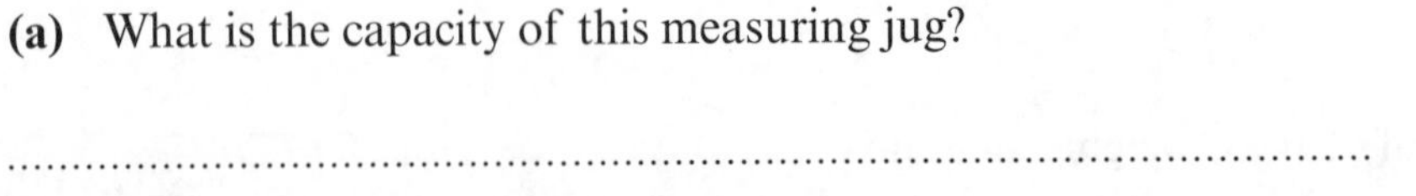

....

(b) What is the volume of the water in the measuring jug?

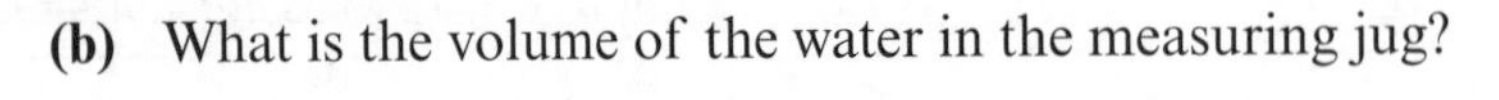

....

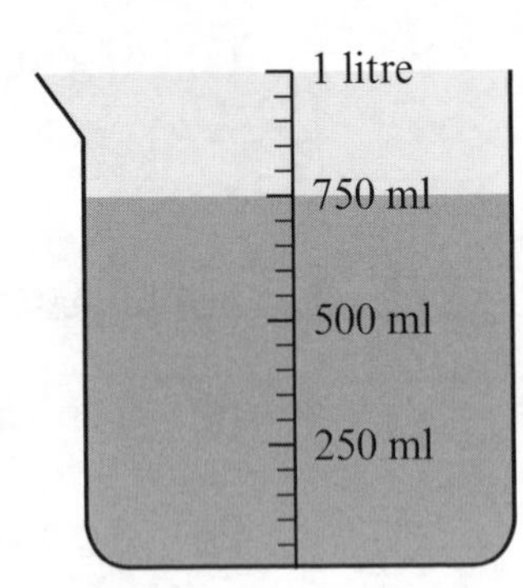

3 Write a unit for each measurement. You could choose an imperial unit or a metric unit.

(a) the volume of water in a fish tank ....

(b) the volume of lemonade in a glass ....

(c) the volume of fuel in a car's fuel tank ....

4 Which capacity is larger, 20 litres or 20 millilitres?

....

5 Order these capacities from smallest to largest: 60 litres, 6 millilitres, 6 litres

....

6 Put a tick in the box by the capacity each container is most likely to hold.

(a)

☐ 2 pints

☐ 20 pints

☐ 200 pints

(b)

☐ 40 litres

☐ 4 litres

☐ 40 ml

(c)

☐ 20 litres

☐ 20 ml

☐ 200 ml

Capacity calculations

1 Write a number to complete the sentence.

There are .... millilitres in 1 litre.

GUIDED **2** Convert these amounts to the units given.

(a) 7 litres to millilitres $7 \times 1000 =$ ....

(b) 4 litres to millilitres ....

3 Find the total of these capacities. Give your answers in millilitres.

Remember to write the units.

(a) 2 litres, 6 litres and 400 ml

....

(b) 9 litres, 250 ml and 500 ml

....

4 Which is the smaller capacity?

Start by converting litres to millilitres.

(a) 8500 ml or 8 litres ....

(b) 4.5 litres or 4350 ml ....

5 Donna wants to drink 3 litres of water on Monday. She drinks a litre in the morning, two 500 ml bottles of water in the afternoon, and 660 ml in the evening. Does she drink 3 litres of water on Monday?

Don't just answer 'yes' or 'no'. You need to show your working then write a conclusion.

....

....

6 Oliver has 2 litres of apple juice and some cups. Each cup will hold 200 ml apple juice.

(a) How many cups can he fill with the apple juice?

....

(b) Oliver drinks 400 ml apple juice. How much does he have left?

....

Had a go ☐ Nearly there ☐ Nailed it! ☐

Money

1 Complete these statements.

(a) The symbol '£' represents ....

(b) £1 = ... pence

GUIDED **2** Write down the calculations used to convert between the units in each pair.

(a) pounds to pence × ....

(b) pence to pounds ÷ ....

3 Write these amounts in numbers, using the '£' symbol.

(a) eight pounds and sixty-seven pence ....

(b) seventeen pounds and eight pence ....

(c) 28p ....

(d) 5462p ....

4 Convert these amounts into pence.

(a) £0.04 ....

(b) £0.83 ....

(c) £11.01 ....

5 Write the following amounts in order from smallest to largest.

(a) £3.58, 85p, £3.85, 58p, £0.90

....

(b) 32p, £32, £32.01, £32.10, 320p

....

6 Roger has five one pound coins. He needs to buy face wash, which costs £5.01, aftershave, which costs £5.10, and hair gel, which costs £4.99.

Which item can he afford to buy? Explain your answer.

....

....

Money calculations

1 Xavier buys some fruit. He buys three mangoes for £2.79 and an apple for 85p. Xavier pays with a £5 note. How much change does he get?

....

2 Ravina was on the social committee in her office. She had an annual budget of £325. She spent £192 on an event. How much money does she have left?

....

3 In the canteen at work, Bart bought a slice of cake for 95p, a mug of tea for £1.49 and a coffee. He paid with a £5 note and received 40p in change. Bart works out that the coffee cost £2.49. Is he correct? Explain your answer.

....

....

4 Zebedee needs to buy three patio chairs. He sees these offers on two different websites.

Offer A: One patio chair £16.50, buy three only £15 each

Offer B: One patio chair £16.50, buy three and get £5 off

Which offer will cost Zebedee the least?

....

5 Marina works in a beauty salon. She needs to buy one bottle each of shampoo, conditioner and hair serum. She sees the products listed in the wholesaler's catalogue.

This week, the wholesaler is offering all three products for a total price of £6

How much will Marina save?

Hair products	
Shampoo	£4.00
Conditioner	£3.95
Hair serum	£4.75

....

6 Coffee capsules are sold in two different sizes of box. A small box of 20 capsules costs £10. A large box of 50 capsules costs £15.

(a) What is the cost per capsule if you buy a small box? ....

(b) What is the cost per capsule if you buy a large box? ....

(c) Which box is better value for money? ....

Had a go ☐ Nearly there ☐ Nailed it! ☐

Problem-solving practice

1 Julia is planning a trip to a theme park for a group of 30 people. They can travel there by train or coach.

This table shows information about the costs.

Train	Coach	
£5 per person	25 seats	£145.00
	35 seats	£149.00
	55 seats	£195.00

Work out the cheapest way to travel.

....

2 The total weight of five metal balls is shown on this weighing scale.

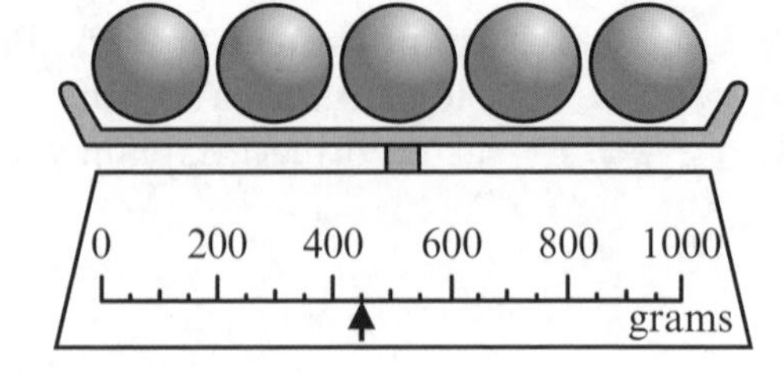

(a) What is the total weight of the five metal balls?

....

(b) Each metal ball has the same weight. Work out the weight of one metal ball.

....

(c) Draw an arrow on the scale to mark the weight of 10 metal balls.

3 Lewis buys a cottage. The lawn in his back garden is rectangular. It has a length of 9 m and a width of 6 m. Lewis wants to buy scallop edgings for his lawn. Each scallop edging is 1 m long. The total length of the scallop edgings need to be equal to the total distance around the lawn.

(a) How many scallop edgings does Lewis need?

....

(b) Each scallop edging costs £4. What is the total cost of the scallop edgings? Show a check of your answer.

....

4 Juanita measures out two liquids in jugs. She wants to pour them both into a larger jug.

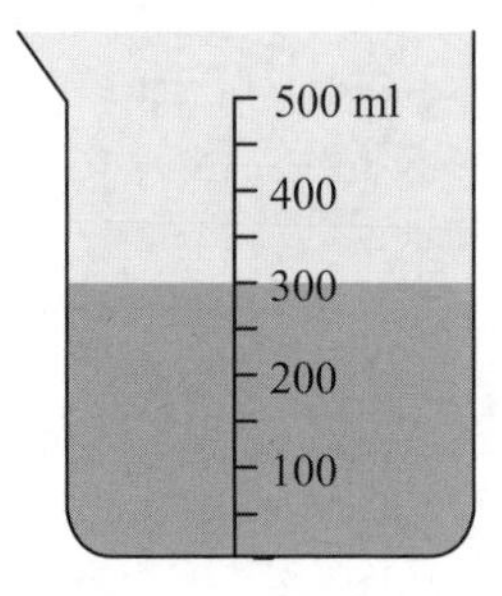

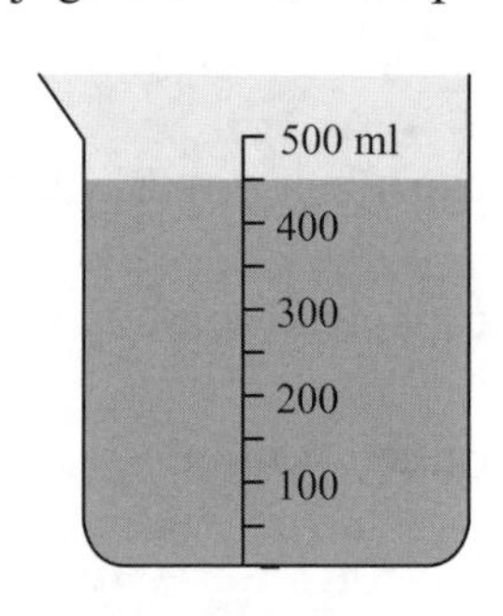

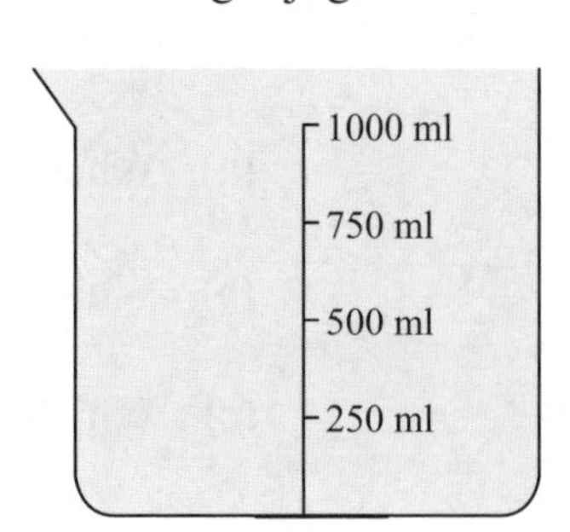

(a) What is the total volume of liquid in the two small jugs?

....

(b) Juanita pours the liquids from the two jugs into the empty jug. Shade the jug to show where the liquid will reach.

Problem-solving practice

1 Leon and his two friends take a 3 litre bottle of water with them to drink at football practice. They also take plastic cups. Each plastic cup holds 200 ml when it is full.

How many cups can they fill from the 3 litre bottle of water?

....

2 Lisa wants to go out at the weekend. She will either go bowling or go to see a play at the theatre. She will have something to eat and drink, and will hire a taxi to get there.
This table gives information about the prices.

Bowling		**Theatre**	
ticket £11.50	food £4.50	ticket £10.00	food £5.95
drink £1.10	taxi £4.00	drink £2.25	taxi £4.00

Lisa wants to spend the smallest possible amount of money. Should she go bowling or go to the theatre?

....

....

3 This map shows some routes from Frank's home to the zoo.

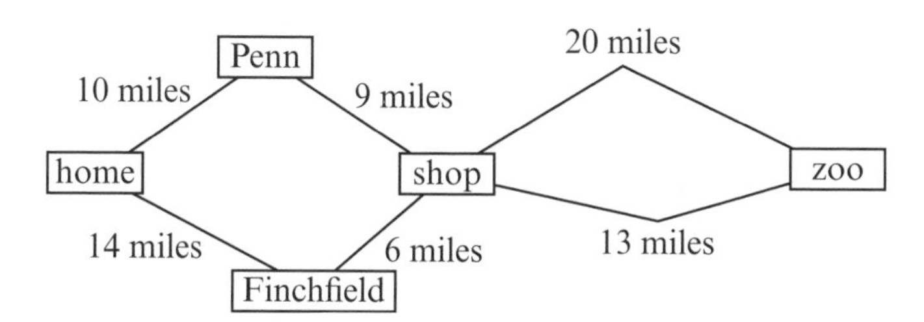

Frank wants to choose the shortest route from home to the zoo.

(a) How many miles is the shortest route from Frank's home to the zoo?

....

(b) Use a coloured pen to outline the shortest route on the map.

4 Reshma wants a job in a shop. She wants to earn as much money as she can. Here are two jobs.

Penn Mart	**Shah's Grocery**
28 hours per week	Tuesday to Friday
Pay: £12 an hour	Pay: £85 for each day

Which job pays more money each week?

....

Had a go ☐ Nearly there ☐ Nailed it! ☐

Angles

1 Which of these angles are right angles? Write the letters on the answer line.

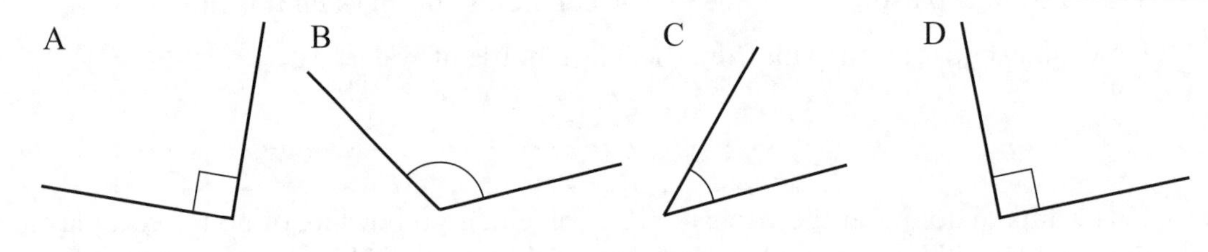

....

2 Write down the number of right angles in each shape.

(a) 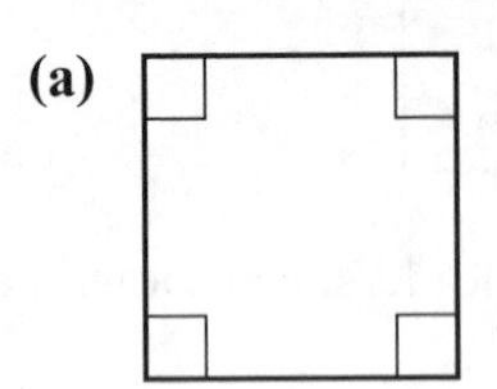 **(b)** 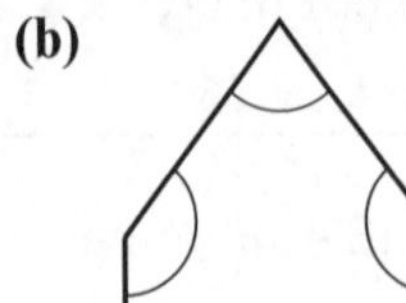 **(c)** 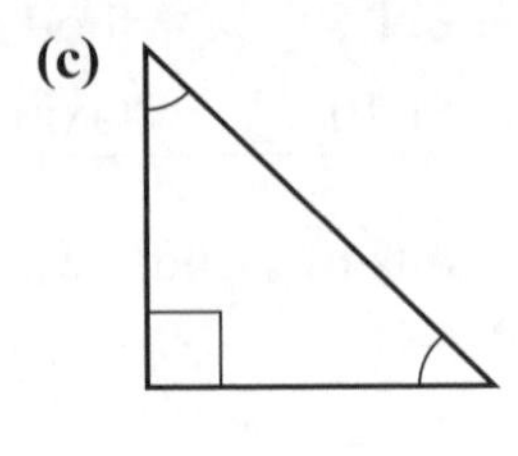

....

3 On this circle, draw where the arrow would be after a half turn.

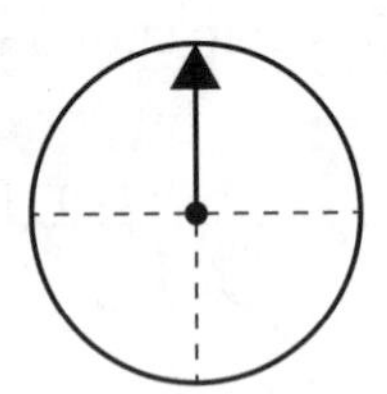

4 Here are three shapes.

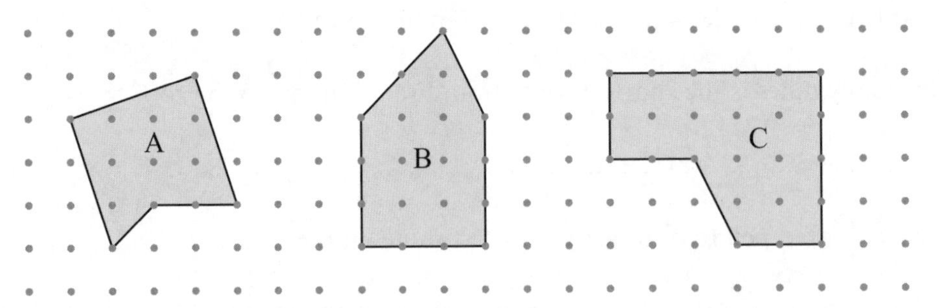

(a) Tick the largest angle in shape A.

(b) Tick the smallest angle in shape B.

(c) How many right angles does shape C have? ....

Symmetry

1 These shapes have lines of symmetry. Draw the lines of symmetry as indicated.

(a) exactly **one** line of symmetry

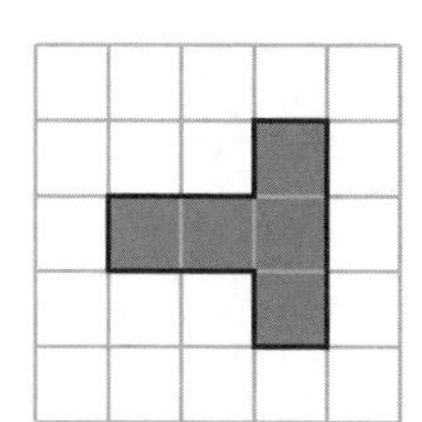

(b) exactly **two** lines of symmetry

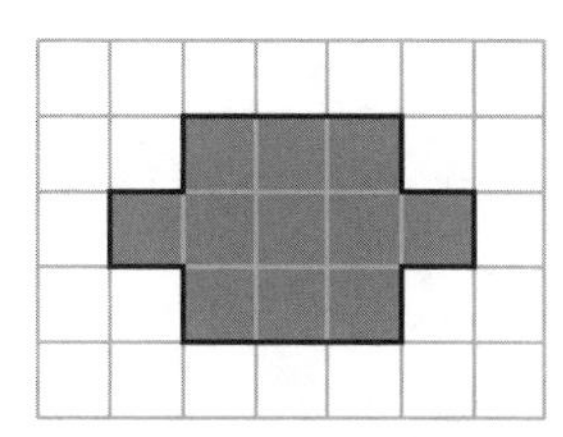

2 Draw one line of symmetry on each of these designs.

(a)

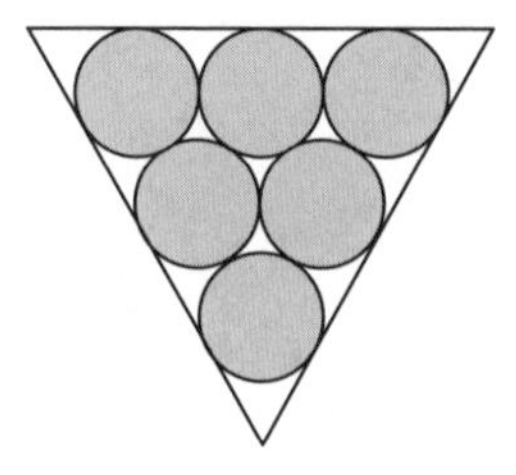

(b)

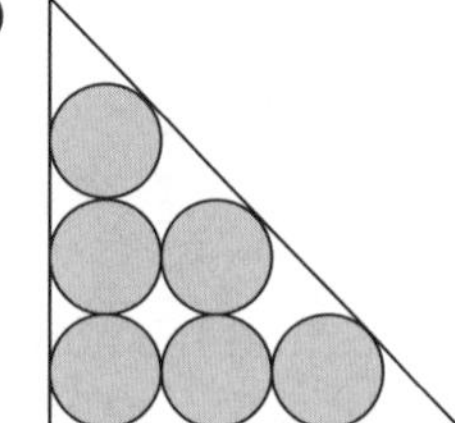

(c)

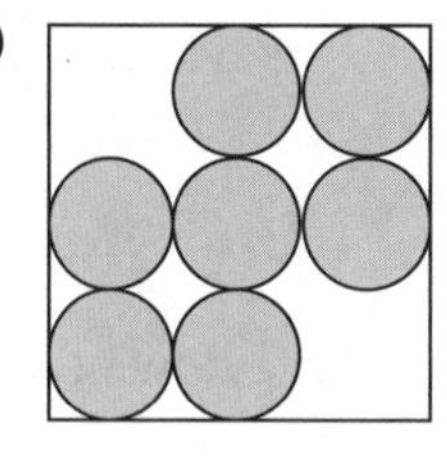

3 Here are four shapes.

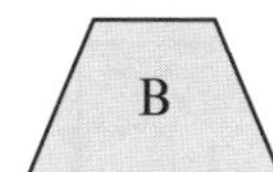

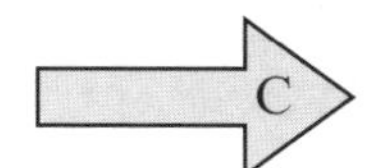

Write down the letter of a shape that has:

(a) **no** lines of symmetry ....

(b) exactly **one** line of symmetry ....

(c) exactly **two** lines of symmetry. ....

4 Here are five shapes on a square grid.

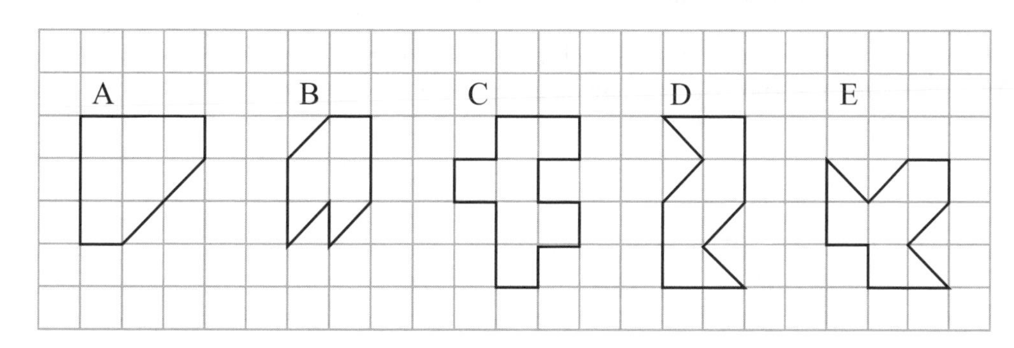

(a) Write down the letters of the shapes that have a line of symmetry.

....

(b) Write down the letters of the shapes that do not have a line of symmetry.

....

Had a go ☐ Nearly there ☐ Nailed it! ☐

2D shapes

1 Write down the mathematical name of each shape.

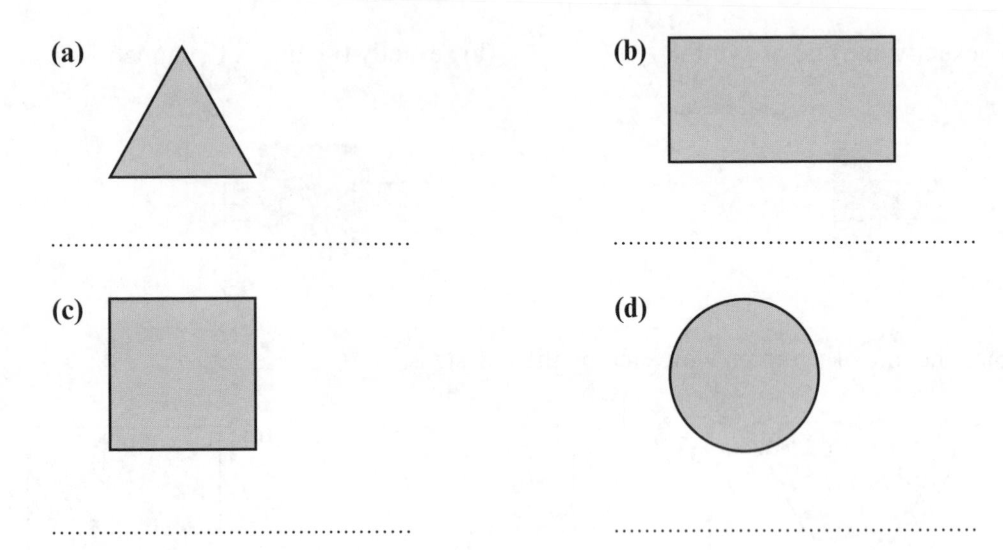

2 Write down the number of sides and the number of angles for each shape.

	Triangle	Square	Rectangle	Circle
number of angles				
number of sides				

3 Name the shapes that are described below.

Description	Shape
This shape has four straight sides and four right angles. All the sides are the same length.	
This shape has three straight sides and three angles.	
This shape has one curved side. It has no angles.	
This shape has four straight sides and four right angles. Two sides are long and two sides are short.	

3D shapes

GUIDED **1** Draw an arrow from each shape to its mathematical name.

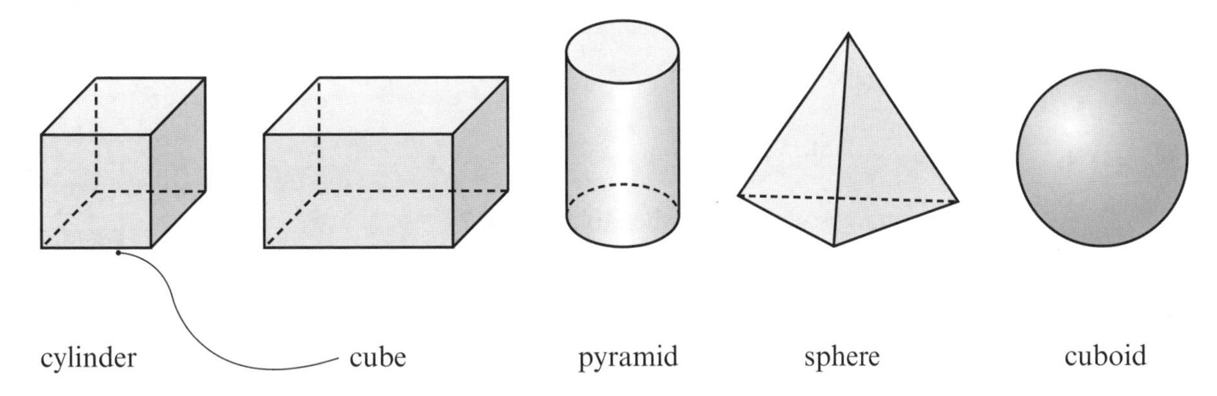

cylinder cube pyramid sphere cuboid

GUIDED **2** Complete the table.

	3D shape	Number of faces	Number of edges	Number of corners
(a)	cube	6	12	8
(b)	cuboid			
(c)	square-based pyramid			
(d)	tetrahedron			
(e)	triangular prism			

3 Here is a diagram of a 3D prism.

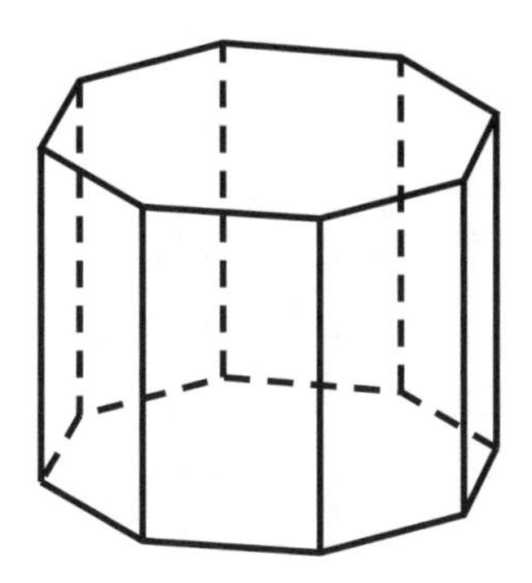

Write down the number of:

(a) faces ....

(b) edges ....

(c) corners ....

Had a go ☐ Nearly there ☐ Nailed it! ☐

Using plans

1 Robert is designing his dining room at home. He makes a plan of the room. There is already a table in the room.

table
door
window

(a) What shape is the table?

....

(b) How many squares does the table take up?

....

(c) Robert wants to put a mat in the corner in front of the door.
The mat is square. It is half as large as the table. Draw the mat on the plan.

2 Pam has a pond and a flowerbed in her garden.
She has a plan of the garden.

flowerbed
pond

(a) What shape is the pond?

....

(b) Pam wants to put a greenhouse in her garden. It will be the same size as her flowerbed. It must not touch the pond or the flowerbed. Draw the greenhouse on the plan.

3 Danielle and three of her friends want to go to the theatre together. The white squares in this plan show available seats and grey squares show seats that are already reserved.

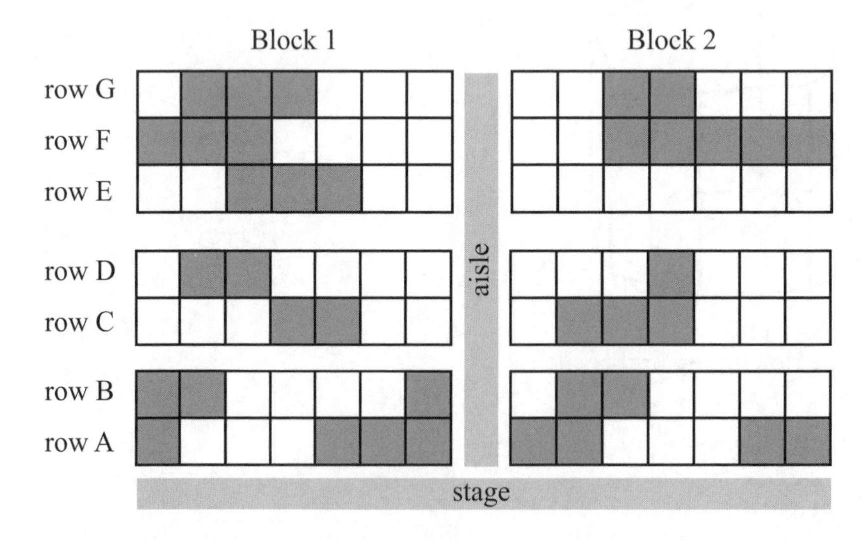

All four friends want to sit together on the same row. They need to be as close as possible to the stage. They prefer seats that are close to the aisle.

Which block and which row should they sit in?

Block .... row ....

Problem-solving practice

1 Helena is the owner of a cafe. She has tables in three different shapes.

Write down the name of each shape and how many right angles each shape has.

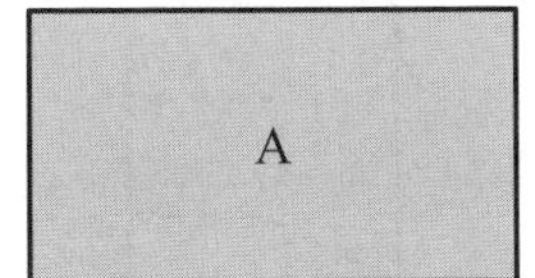

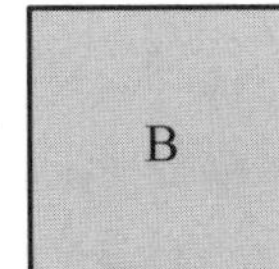

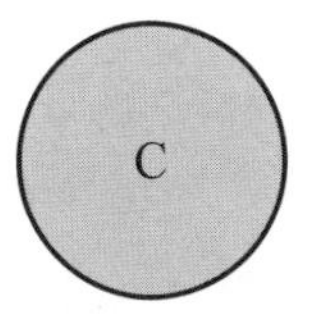

	A	**B**	**C**
name of shape			
number of right angles			

2 Ned buys a box of tiles. This diagram shows the shape of the box.

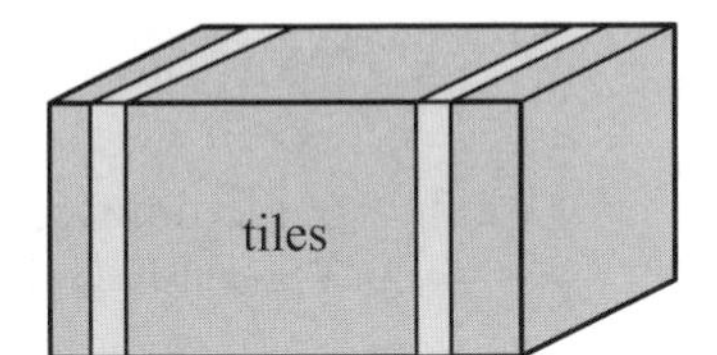

(a) Write the name of the shape of the box. ....

(b) Write down the number of:

(i) faces .... **(ii)** edges .... **(iii)** vertices ....

3 Here are three quadrilaterals.

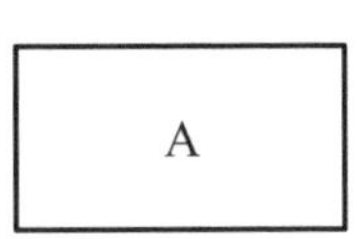

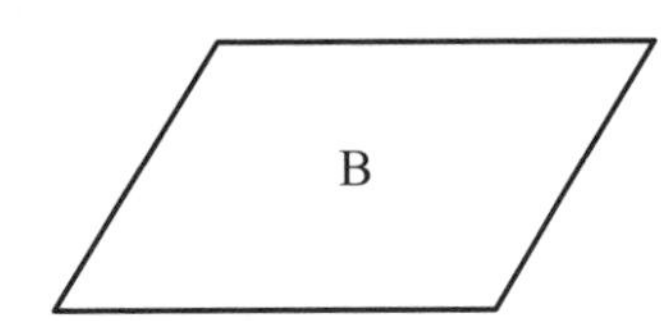

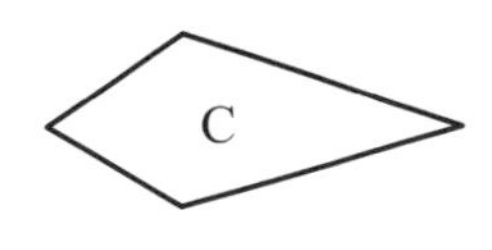

Write down the letter of the quadrilateral that has:

(a) **no** lines of symmetry ....

(b) exactly **one** line of symmetry ....

(c) exactly **two** lines of symmetry ....

(d) at least one right angle. ....

Had a go ☐ Nearly there ☐ Nailed it! ☐

Problem-solving practice

1 Gloria works in a card shop and needs to choose a gift box to stock. The warehouse has these three gift boxes. Write down the name of the shape of each box.

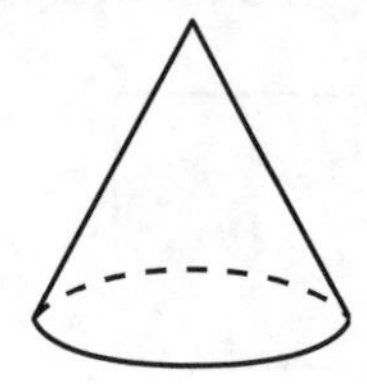

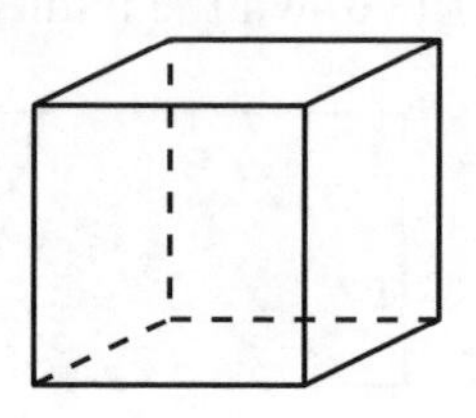

....

2 Sandeep is choosing a design for a company logo. The design must have exactly two lines of symmetry and at least one right angle.

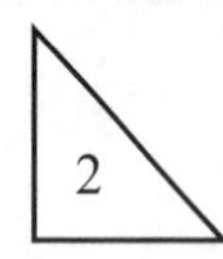

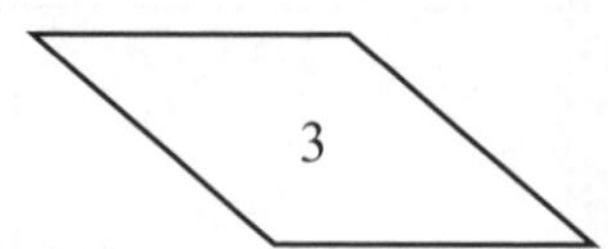

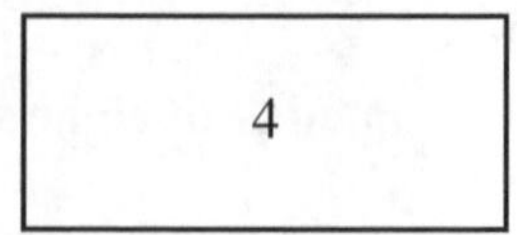

Write the number of the design that Sandeep should use. ....

3 Malcolm wants to put a table in his bedroom. He draws a plan of the floor on a grid. The table is the same size as the drawers.

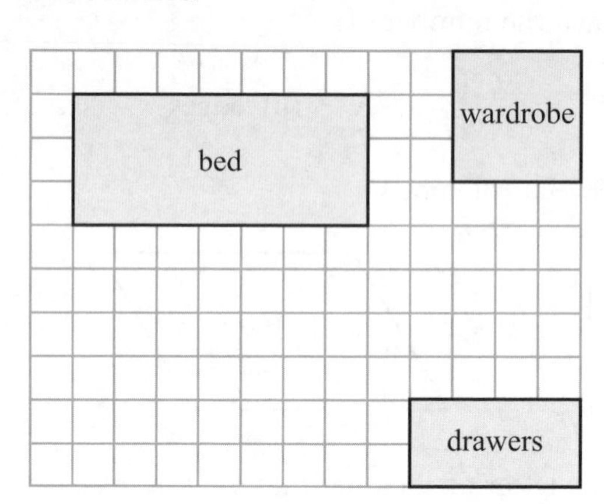

Draw the table onto the plan.

Lists

1 Tracey went shopping. She bought 2 necklaces for £3.40 each, 1 scarf for £5.60 and 1 bag for £7.90

Work out her total bill.

....

2 Joan buys some food from her local shop. She receives this receipt.

bread	£1.20
milk	£1.80
bacon	£2.60
sausages	£2.75

Joan pays with a £10 note. She is given £2.65 change. Is this correct?

....

....

3 Fred wants to tile his bathroom. He sees the following prices in a catalogue.

grout	£7.50 for each bag
plain tiles	20p each
patterned tiles	50p each

He buys three bags of grout, 120 plain tiles and 30 patterned tiles. Work out the total cost.

....

4 Jeff owns a small business. He receives these quotes from three carpenters to carry out some repairs at his unit.

Woody's		Marwaha Joinery		Akaal Limited	
call out charge	£30.00	total labour	£79.00	call out charge	£20.00
total labour	£50.00	parts/materials	£14.00	total labour	£60.00
parts/materials	£15.00	total exc. VAT	£93.00	parts/materials	£10.00
total exc. VAT	£95.00	VAT	£18.60	total exc. VAT	£90.00
VAT	£19.00			VAT	£18.00

Jeff wants to use the carpenter who gave the cheapest quote. Which carpenter should he choose?

....

Had a go ☐ Nearly there ☐ Nailed it! ☐

Tables

1 This table gives information about the prices for renting different types of boat for an hour at different times of year.

Type of boat	Price in June	Price in September
speedboat	£14.70	£11.40
kayak	£7.20	£5.80
rowing boat	£5.90	£4.00

(a) In June, how much does it cost to rent a rowing boat for an hour?

....

(b) In September, how much more does it cost to rent a speedboat than a kayak for an hour?

....

(c) Is it more expensive to rent a kayak in June or to rent a speedboat in September?

....

2 Nathan did a survey to find out how many of his pupils went to Paris and how many went to Rome on their school trip. This table shows the results.

	Paris	Rome
boys	15	18
girls	20	27

(a) How many pupils went to Paris? ....

(b) How many boys took part in the survey? ....

(c) How many pupils took part in the survey? ....

3 Raymond needs to buy 52 toys for a children's activity weekend. The toys cost £3.00 each. This table shows information about the delivery charges.

What is the total cost for 52 toys including the delivery charge?

Number of toys ordered	Delivery charge
0–10	£6.00
11–20	£7.50
21–40	£9.00
41–60	£10.50
61 or more	£12.00

....

Tally charts

1 Jim goes to a county show. This incomplete table gives information about the types of displays at the show.

卌 represents 5

Display	animals	traction engines	fruit and veg	country crafts
Tally	卌	卌 卌		卌 卌 II
Frequency			6	

(a) Complete the tally and frequency columns on the table.

(b) How many traction engine displays are there? ....

(c) How many displays were there in total? ....

2 Ignacio asked 20 adults which activity they would prefer to do on an activity holiday. The results are listed below.

rafting, sewing, climbing, climbing, rafting, hiking, rafting, rafting, hiking, climbing, climbing, climbing, rafting, climbing, hiking, rafting, climbing, rafting, hiking, rafting

Preferred activity	rafting	sewing	climbing	hiking
Tally				
Frequency				

(a) Complete the table.

(b) Which was the most popular activity? ....

(c) How many more adults chose rafting than hiking? ....

3 Ranjit asks each of his friends which type of film they like best. Here are the results:

romance, horror, romance, documentary, romance, romance, comedy, horror, romance, romance, comedy, comedy, romance, documentary, comedy, horror, comedy, comedy, romance, comedy, horror, romance, romance, romance, romance, documentary

Type of film	**Tally**	**Frequency**
horror	IIII	
documentary	III	3
comedy		7
romance	卌 卌 II	12

(a) Complete the table.

(b) Which was the least popular type of film? ....

(c) How many more people liked comedy than documentary? ....

(d) Work out the total number of friends Ranjit asked. ....

Had a go ☐ Nearly there ☐ Nailed it! ☐

Reading bar charts

1 Lyla surveys the materials that houses in her village are made of. She displays the results in this bar chart.

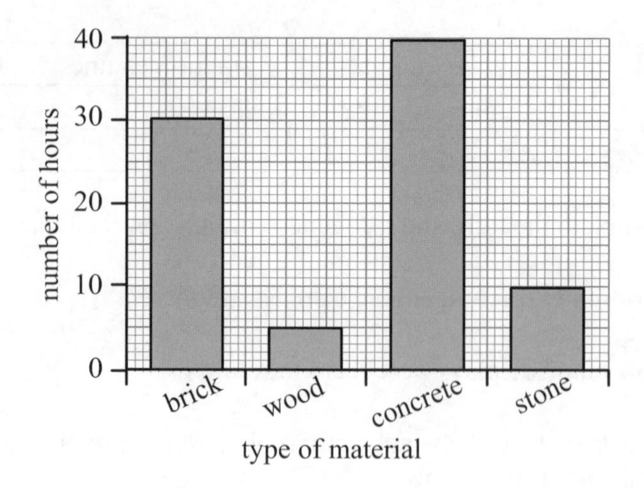

(a) What is the least common building material? ....

(b) How many stone houses are there? ....

(c) How many more concrete houses than brick houses are there?

....

2 This bar chart shows the numbers of devices sold one Friday at Robin's shop.

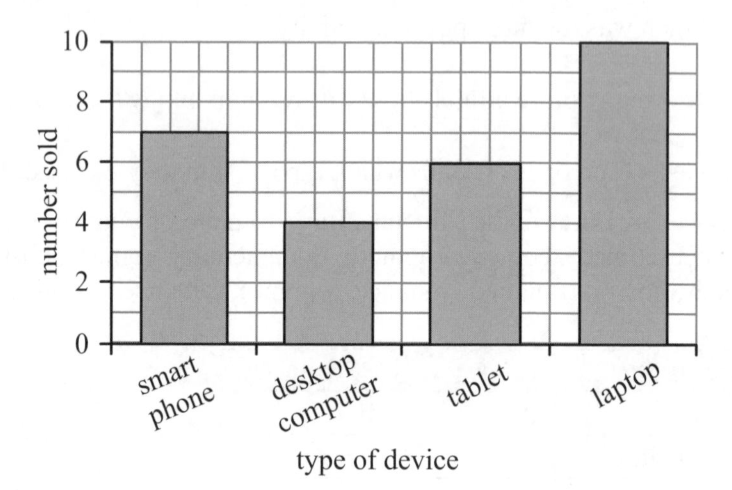

(a) How many laptops did he sell? ....

(b) Which device did Robin sell the fewest of? ....

(c) How many more smartphones than desktop computers were sold?

....

(d) How many devices were sold altogether?

....

Completing a bar chart

1 A company has 50 part-time employees. This table gives information about the number of employees who worked on each of 5 days last week.

Day	Mon	Tue	Wed	Thu	Fri
Number of employees	10	25	45	40	15

Complete the bar chart to show this information.

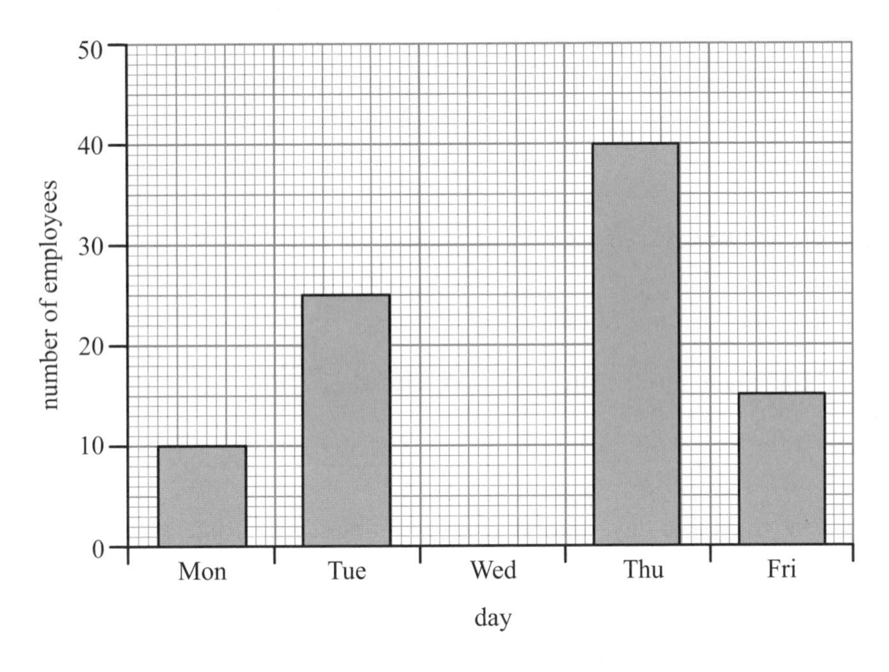

2 The table shows the numbers of different types of bird kept at a zoo.

Bird	finch	canary	parrot	penguin	owl
Number	12	15	26	37	8

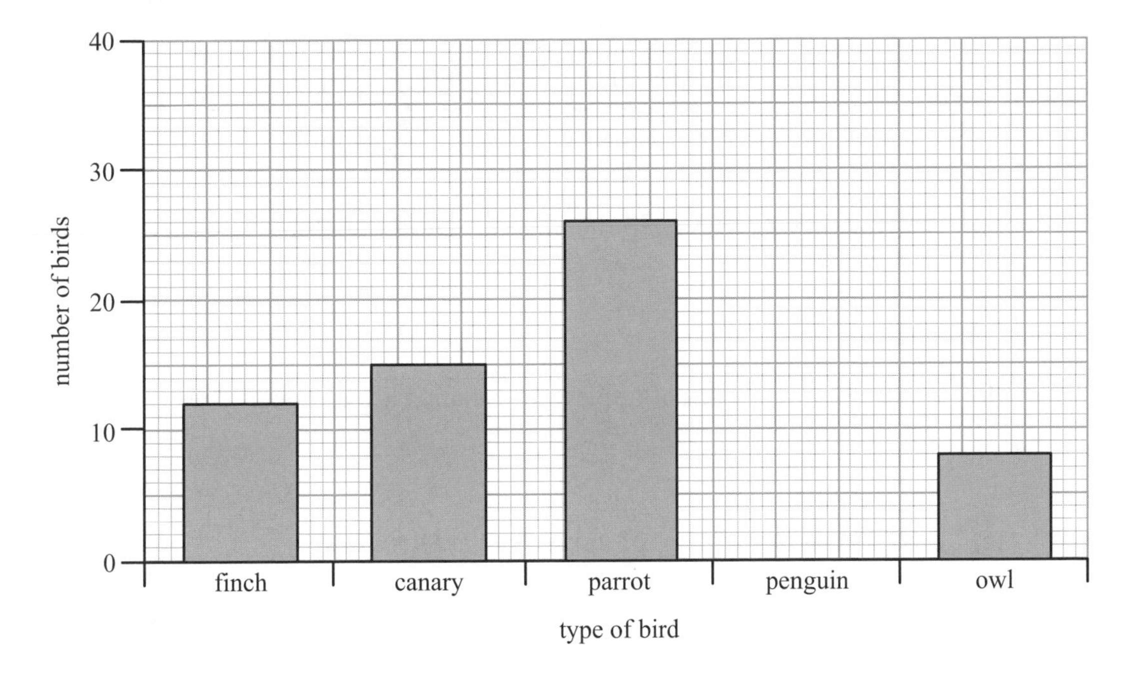

Complete the bar chart to show the number of penguins.

Had a go ☐ **Nearly there** ☐ **Nailed it!** ☐

Reading pictograms

1 This pictogram shows information about the numbers of customers who were served at a cafe from Monday to Friday one week.

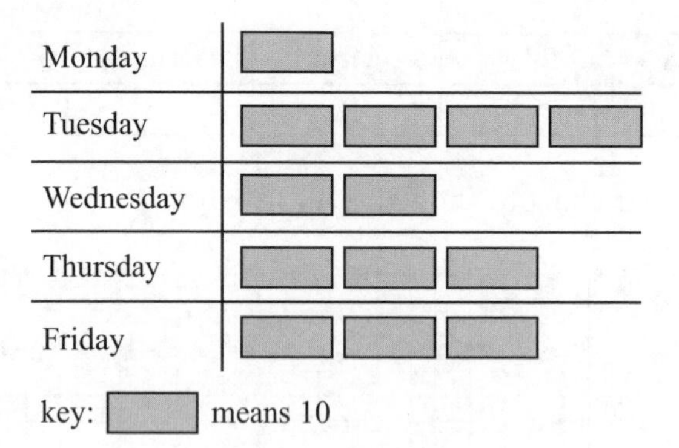

(a) How many customers were served on Tuesday?

....

(b) How many more customers were served on Thursday than on Wednesday?

....

(c) On which two days were the same number of customers served?

....

2 This pictogram shows the numbers of bags of apples sold in five grocery shops in one day.

Fred's
Fruitlands
Vegworld
Quickshop
Sophie's

(a) Which shop sold the greatest number of bags of apples?

....

(b) Vegworld sold 12 bags of apples. How many bags of apples does each 🍎 represent?

....

(c) Find the number of bags of apples sold at Quickshop.

....

Reading pie charts

1 This pie chart shows information about the types of bird Simon spotted in his garden over one hour.

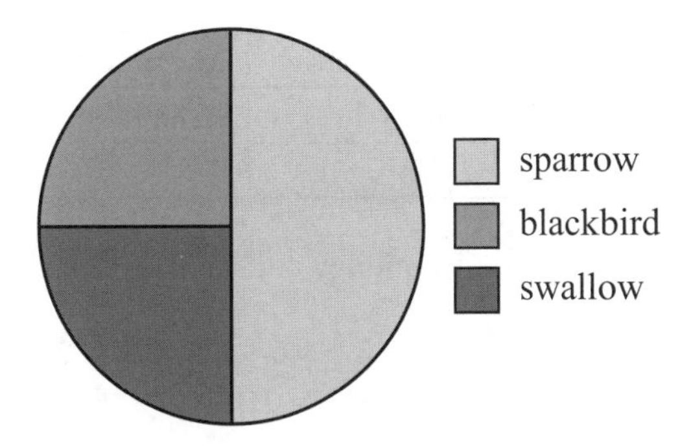

(a) Which bird did Simon spot the most?

Which is the largest segment in the pie chart?

....

(b) What fraction of the birds he spotted were blackbirds?

....

(c) Simon saw 4 swallows. How many birds did he see in total?

....

2 These pie charts show information about the items Grace sold in her gift shop on Saturday and Sunday.

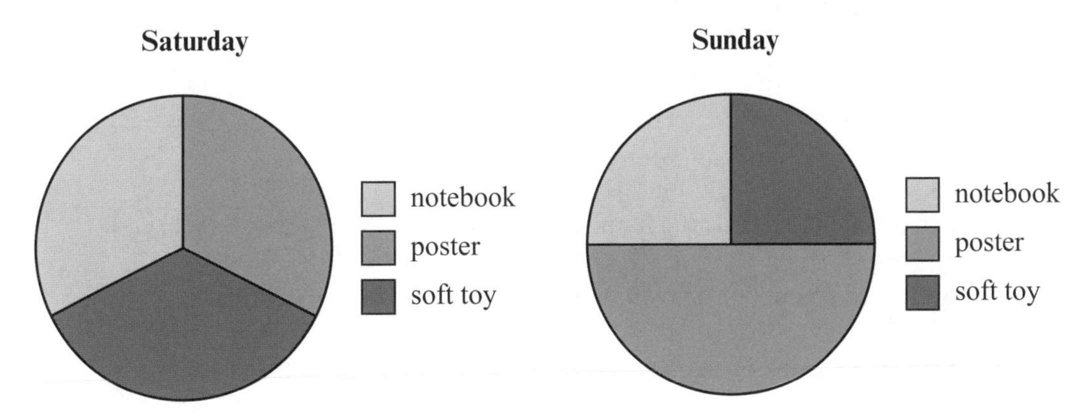

(a) What item did Grace sell the most of on Sunday?

....

(b) What fraction of the items sold on Saturday were notebooks?

....

(c) On Sunday, Grace sold 12 notebooks. How many posters did she sell on Sunday?

....

Had a go ☐ Nearly there ☐ Nailed it! ☐

Problem-solving practice

GUIDED **1** This table gives information about the different types of sandwiches sold during lunch time one day.

Sandwich	ham and tomato	egg and cheese	cheese and pickle	tuna mayo
Tally	卌 卌 卌 卌 II	卌 卌 卌 III		卌 卌 I
Frequency	22		9	

(a) Complete the tally and frequency columns on the table.

(b) How many ham and tomato and egg and cheese sandwiches were sold in total?

22 + ...

(c) How many sandwiches were sold during this lunch time in total?

....

2 Matthew wants to do a charity walk. He needs to buy some equipment first.

This table shows the quantities of the items he needs and the price per item in two different shops.

Item	Quantity needed	Do Camping	Heptathlon
water bottle	2	£6.50	£6.75
boots	1	£35.80	£32.99

Matthew wants to buy everything from the same shop. He wants to spend as little as possible. Which shop should he buy his items from?

....

....

3 A cafe owner records the number of drinks he has sold over a weekend.

Saturday: 65 cups of tea, 50 mugs of coffee and 40 milkshakes

Sunday: 70 cups of tea, 45 mugs of coffee and 25 milkshakes

Draw a table to show this information.

Problem-solving practice

1 This pictogram shows the numbers of boxes of chocolates a shop sold last week from Monday to Friday.

Monday
Tuesday
Wednesday
Thursday
Friday

key: [symbol] means 12 boxes of chocolates

(a) How many boxes of chocolates were sold on Monday?

....

(b) How many boxes of chocolates were sold on Wednesday?

....

(c) How many more boxes of chocolates were sold on Friday than were sold on Thursday?

....

(d) How many boxes of chocolate were sold in total?

....

2 Tom carried out a traffic survey. He kept a record of the number of each type of vehicles he saw. This table shows information about the number of types of vehicles over a period of a day.

Type of vehicle	bus	car	motorbike	lorry	van
Frequency	13	32	9	23	27

(a) Complete this bar chart.

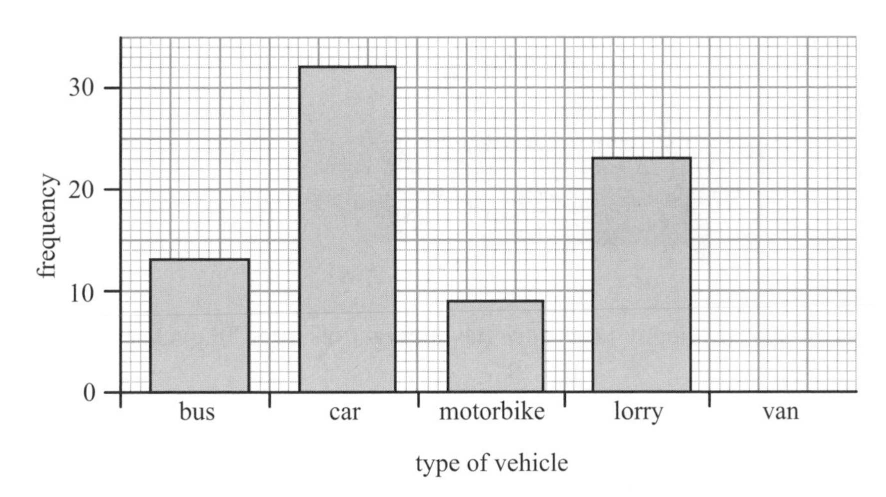

(b) Which type of vehicle did he see three times as often as motorbikes?

....

(c) How many vehicles did Tom see in total?

....

Practice paper

The practice test paper has been written to help you practise what you have learned.
The real test might not look like this.

You have up to 1 hour 30 minutes to answer all the questions.
You can write or draw in the book to show your answers.
You can use a calculator.

1 Planning a concert

Media Promotions organise an annual concert.

People buy tickets to go to the concert. Last year, 435 tickets were sold.

(a) What is 435 to the nearest 100? **(1)**

Write your answer in the box below.

The manager needs to organise some taxis for 50 guests to get to the concert.

The guests will be collected from the railway station.

Each taxi can only seat 7 guests.

(b) How many taxis does the manager need for 50 guests? **(2)**

Write your working and answer in the box below.

The cost of each taxi is £25

Each guest has luggage. The manager has to pay a surcharge on each guest's luggage.

This table shows the cost of the surcharge on the luggage.

Number of taxis hired	1	2	3	4	5	6 or more
Surcharge	£25	£30	£35	£40	£45	£50

(c) Work out the total of the hire cost and the surcharge for the taxis. **(3)**

Write your working and answer in the box below.

2 At the concert

Ashley is at the concert.

He can buy bottles of water from a drinks stall.

He can buy 1 bottle of water or a pack of 3 bottles of water.

These are the prices:

1 bottle (60p)

pack of 3 bottles (£1.50)

(a) Is it cheaper to buy a pack of 3 bottles or to buy 3 individual bottles? **(2)**

Write your working and answer in the box below.

The concert hall has a seating plan.

The number of the seat at the end of each row follows a pattern.

The first five numbers in the pattern are:

12, 24, 36, 48, 60

(b) What is the next number in the pattern? **(1)**

Write your working and answer in the box below.

The middle section of the concert hall seats 180 people.

One-third of the seats are taken up by children.

(c) What is one-third of 180? **(2)**

Write your working and answer in the box below.

(d) Show a calculation to check your answer. **(2)**

Write your working and answer in the box below.

At the concert, all children were given a small carton of juice.

Here is the carton.

(e) What is the name of the shape of the carton of juice? **(1)**

Write your answer in the box below.

The concert is going to have four performances.

DJ Fun	Magic Man	Animation	Comedy
9.30 p.m.	19:15	20:45	8.00 p.m.

(f) List the four performances in the correct time order. **(1)**

Write your answer in the box below.

3 On the way home

The map shows some routes from the concert hall to Ashley's home.

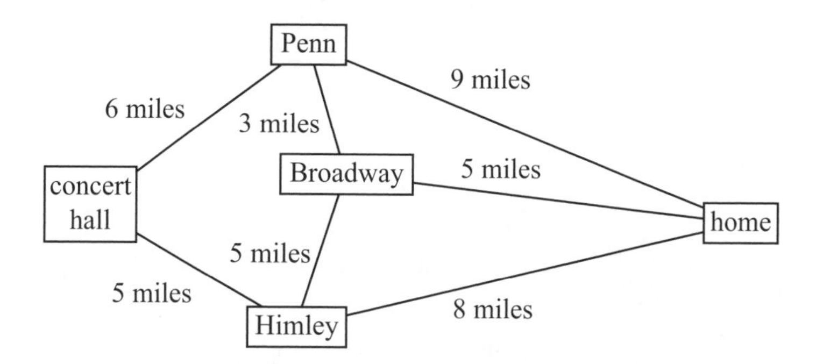

(a) Work out the shortest route from the concert hall to Ashley's home. **(2)**

Write your working and answer in the box below.

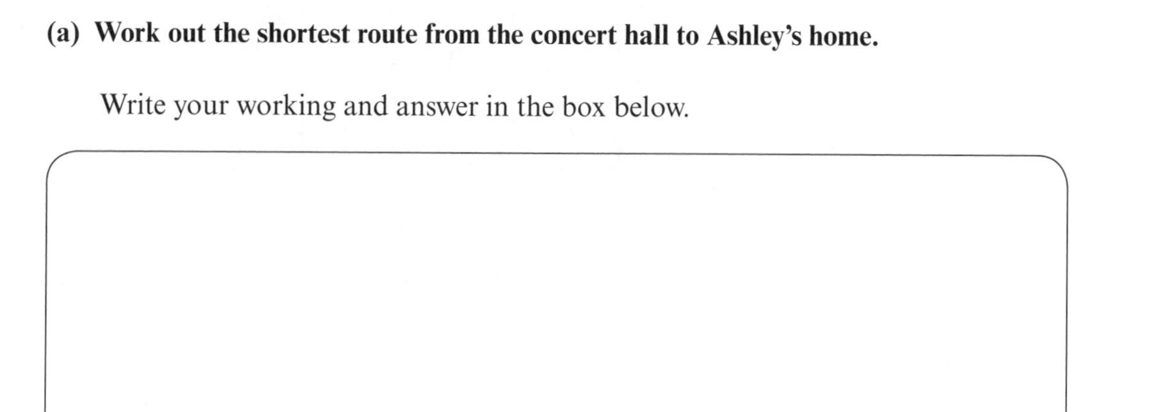

After the concert, Ashley goes to sleep at 11.30 p.m.

He sets his alarm clock for 7.30 a.m.

(b) How many hours are there between 11.30 p.m. and 7.30 a.m.? **(1)**

Write your working and answer in the box below.

4 Finances

This bar chart shows the amounts of money the promotion company made from selling different types of ticket.

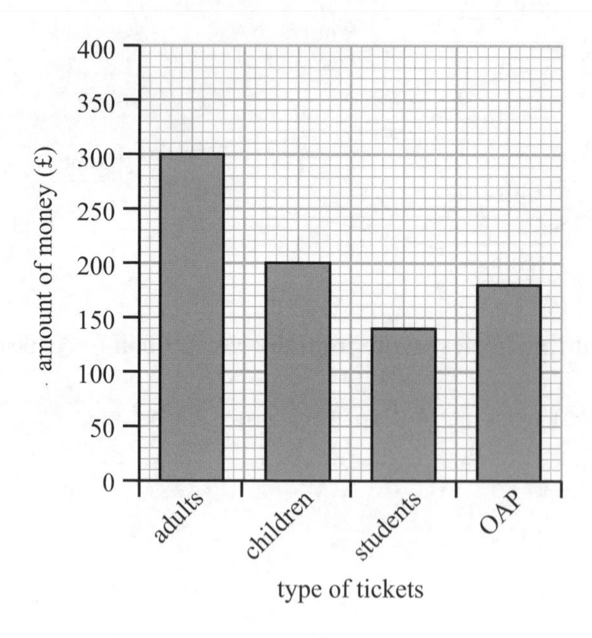

(a) Which type of ticket made the most money? **(2)**

Write your answer in the box below.

(b) How much money did the promotion company earn in total ticket sales? **(2)**

Write your working and answer in the box below.

ANSWERS

NUMBER

1 Whole numbers

1. **(b)** Any three-digit number with 5 tens, such as 451 (four hundred and fifty-one)
   (c) Any two-digit number with 2 units, such as 92 (ninety-two)
2. **(a)** seventeen **(b)** one hundred and sixty-nine
   (c) nine hundred and seventy-four
3. **(a)** 28 **(b)** 142 **(c)** 805
4. **(a)** 50 **(b)** 500 **(c)** 50
5. 234 as 4 is a unit
6. **(a)** Donald **(b)** Carl

2 Comparing numbers

1. **(b)** 854 **(c)** 993
2. **(a)** 397 **(b)** 735 **(c)** 228
3. **(a)** 51 **(b)** 129
4. **(a)** 78 **(b)** 543
5. **(a)** 89, 96, 98, 114, 124, 210
   (b) 239, 329, 392, 923, 932
6. **(a)** 10 **(b)** 9 **(c)** 8

3 Adding

1. +
2. **(b)** 737 **(c)** 819
3. **(a)** 97 **(b)** 685 **(c)** 484
4. 232
5. 372
6. 437 miles
7. 596
8. £670

4 Subtracting

1. −
2. **(b)** 169 **(c)** 317
3. **(a)** 92 **(b)** 514 **(c)** 458
4. 19
5. 103
6. £14
7. 115

5 Multiplication

1. ×
2. **(b)** 120 **(c)** 96
3. **(a)** 90 **(b)** 120 **(c)** 160
4. 200
5. £30
6. **(a)** 12 **(b)** 30
7. **(a)** 600 m **(b)** 750 m **(c)** 4500 m

6 Division

1. ÷
2. **(b)** 7 **(c)** 12 **(d)** 15
3. **(a)** 9 **(b)** 30 **(c)** 36 **(d)** 39
4. £80
5. 32 miles
6. £18
7. **(a)** 7 **(b)** 28
8. 168

7 Multiplying and dividing by 10, 100 and 1000

1. **(a)** 990 **(b)** 8
2. 2 metres
3. £670
4. **(a)** £800 **(b)** £8.00

8 Remainders

1. **(b)** 4 **(c)** 4
2. 9
3. 11
4. 17
5. 5
6. 2
7. No, he needs 20 packs.
8. Each pupil will receive five sweets and she will have three left over.
9. 9

9 Choosing the right order

1. £7
2. £300
3. **(a)** 162 **(b)** 21
4. **(a)** 300 **(b)** 10
5. **(a)** 780 **(b)** 7

10 Using a calculator

1. **(a)** 842 **(b)** 56 **(c)** 337 **(d)** 30
2. £39
3. **(a)** £1,200 **(b)** 350
4. Alex spends £45 more than his monthly income.
5. £1,360
6. £81
7. 1120 cups

11 Multiples

1.

2	4	6	8	10	12	14	16	18	20
3	6	9	12	15	18	21	24	27	30
4	8	12	16	20	24	28	32	36	40
5	10	15	20	25	30	35	40	45	50
6	12	18	24	30	36	42	48	54	60
7	14	21	28	35	42	49	56	63	70
8	16	24	32	40	48	56	64	72	80
9	18	27	36	45	54	63	72	81	90
10	20	30	40	50	60	70	80	90	100

2. **(a)** 3 or 15 **(b)** 12 or 24
3. **(a)** any two even numbers or any two odd numbers
   (b) 40
4. **(a)** 5 or 25 **(b)** 6 and 12 **(c)** 5 and 6
5. 4 or 5

12 Number patterns

1. (a) 14, 17 (b) 30, 25 (c) 32, 64 (d) 160, 5
2. (a) £30 (b) £35
3. (b) 11 km (b) 21 km
4. £32.75
5. 100 bacteria
6. Tuesday 3, Saturday 7, Wednesday 11, Sunday 15, Thursday 19, Monday 23, Friday 27, Tuesday 31

13 Decimals

1. (b) 123 and 124 (c) 28 and 29
2. (a) 16 (b) 83
3. (a) seven tenths (b) seven hundredths (c) seven tens (d) seven units
4. (a) 8.6 (b) 62.3 (c) 56.74
5. (a) 7 — 8 (b) 43 — 44
6. (a) 2 (b) 1 (c) 2 (d) 2

14 Ordering decimals

1. (b) 6.87 (c) 6.40 (d) 8.95 (e) 17.1 (f) same value
2. (a) 0.72, 0.78, 0.81
   (b) 3.74, 4.23, 4.5
   (c) 4.6, 6.04, 6.4
   (d) 0.09, 0.15, 0.8
3. Seamus, Ian, James
4. Achatz, Franklin, Mata
5. C, A, B

15 Fractions

1. $\frac{1}{3}$
2. (a) Any two squares to be shaded
   (b) Any one square to be shaded
3. $\frac{1}{4}$
4. (a) $\frac{1}{2}$ (b) Any two squares to be shaded
5. (a) $\frac{1}{10}$ (b) $\frac{1}{5}$
6. (a) one-third (b) one-sixth
7. $\frac{1}{4}$

16 Types of fractions

1. (a) shaded = $\frac{5}{8}$ or five-eighths

   not shaded = $\frac{3}{8}$ or three-eighths

   (b)

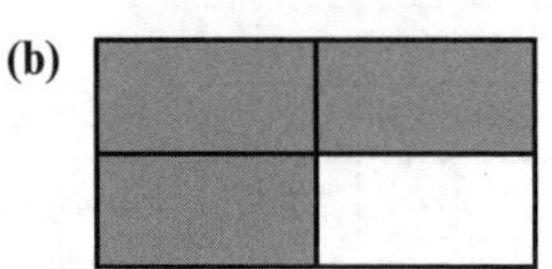

2. $\frac{1}{8}$ or one-eighth
3. $\frac{7}{10}$
4. $\frac{14}{31}$
5. (a) $\frac{15}{20}$ (b) $\frac{5}{20}$
6. $\frac{1}{4}$
7. $\frac{3}{5}$

17 Equivalent fractions

1. Yes.
2. (a) $\frac{1}{2}$ and $\frac{3}{6}$ (b) $\frac{4}{4}$ and $\frac{2}{2}$ (c) $\frac{1}{4}$ and $\frac{2}{8}$
3. (a) $\frac{1}{2}$ (b) $\frac{3}{10}$
4. No, because $\frac{3}{4}$ is not equivalent to $\frac{4}{5}$.
5. (a) Anna: $\frac{1}{4}$

   Bill: $\frac{2}{8}$

   (b) Yes, because $\frac{1}{4}$ and $\frac{2}{8}$ are equivalent.
6. (a) No, because $\frac{2}{5}$ and $\frac{1}{10}$ are not equivalent.
7. She earns more in the factory.

18 Fractions of amounts

1. (a) 15 (b) 20 (c) 32
2. 16
3. £80
4. (a) 12 (b) 30 (c) 78
5. Amy saves £420 and Brian saves £200, so Amy saves more.

19 Rounding whole numbers

1. (a) 10 (b) 20 (c) 60 (d) 200
2. (a) 100 (b) 100 (c) 300 (d) 700
3. 90
4. 60
5. 200
6. Simon 2 points, Peter 0 points
7. Number of men could be 85, number of women could be 55
   85 + 55 = 140, so it may not be true.

20 Rounding money

1. (b) 17 (c) 39
2. (a) £5 (b) £25 (c) £96
3. (b) £123 (c) £654 (d) £985
4. (a) Yes, as the estimate is £10
   (b) No, as the estimate is £19
   (c) Yes, as the estimate is £33

21 Estimating

You might work out your estimates differently, but make sure they are sensible.

1. (a) 140 (b) 860 (c) 800 (d) 10
2. £140
3. £120
4. £10,000
5. 5 cans
6. £3,000
7. (a) 400 g (b) 450

22 Checking your answer

1. (b) correct (c) correct
2. (b) correct (c) correct
   (d) incorrect, 106
3. She is likely to be wrong because $21 \times 9 \approx 20 \times 10 = 200$, which is not close to 69
4. (a) £12.80
   (b) There is more than one sensible way of checking your answer. You could work out $60 \div 5 = 12$ or $12.80 \times 5 = 64$

23 Problem-solving practice

1. Deal A
2. $\frac{1}{3}$ of £15 is £5 and $\frac{1}{2}$ of £8 is £4 so FenceWorld is cheaper.
3. £17.50
4. (a) 157 (b) 11

24 Problem-solving practice

1.

Month	Jan	Feb	Mar	Apr
Number of mortgages	6	12	24	48

2. (a) £50 is a sensible estimate.
   (b) £10 is a sensible estimate.
3. 14.36, 14.56, 14.63

TIME

25 Calendars

1. 1 April
2. (a) 9 days (b) 20 days (c) 24 days
3. (a) 28 (b) Sunday 6 November

26 Units of time

1. (a) 60 (b) 7 (c) 60
2. (b) 180 seconds (c) 240 seconds
3. (a) 15 minutes (b) 45 minutes (c) 120 minutes
4. $1\frac{1}{4}$ hours
5. 2 hours and 30 minutes
6. 4 hours and 15 minutes
7. 1 hour and 45 minutes

27 12-hour clock

1. (b) half (c) three-quarters
2. (a) 7.00 a.m. (b) 4.15 p.m.
   (c) 11.45 p.m. (d) 6.35 a.m.
3. (a)

(b)

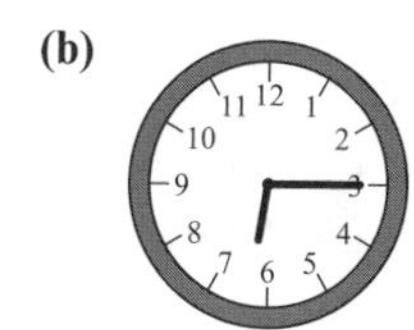

4. (a) 2.15 a.m. (b) 5.30 p.m. (c) 3.00 p.m.
   (d) 7.45 a.m. (e) 12.50 p.m.
5.

28 24-hour clock

1. (b) 14:25 (c) 16:28
   (d) 05:15 (e) 00:05 (f) 12:15
2. (b) 1.16 a.m. (c) 8.35 p.m.
   (d) 6.42 p.m. (e) 11.45 a.m. (f) 4.30 p.m.
3. (a) 07:00 (b) 16:15
   (c) 23:45 (d) 18:35
4. (a)

(b)

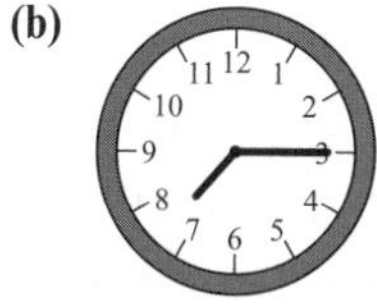

5. (a) 07:45 (b) 12:50 (c) 07:20

29 Time calculations

1. (a) 2 hours 15 minutes (b) 3 hours 45 minutes
   (c) 2 hours 30 minutes
2. (a) 5 p.m. (b) 4 p.m.
3. (a) 19:00 (b) 10:30
4. (a) 20 minutes (b) 21:45
5. 14:50

30 Timetables

1. (a) 06:00 (b) 25 minutes
2. (a) Sunday (b) 12 hours
3. (a) 1 hour 35 minutes (b) 08:45
4. (a) 1 hour 15 minutes (b) 15:15

31 Problem-solving practice

1. (a) 15:00 (b) 17:00
2. 7 hours
3. 2 hours 45 minutes
4. (a) 15 December (b) 28 December

32 Problem-solving practice

1. 17 March
2. (a) 3.30 p.m. (b) 12:45
   (c) Philosophy, Politics, Ethics, Logic
3. (a) 20 minutes (b) 14:05
   (c) 2 hours and 50 minutes (d) 15:50
4. Yes, as the film finishes at 9.45 p.m.

MEASURES

33 Units

1. **length** **temperature** **capacity** **weight**

a measure of how much a container can hold — a measure of how heavy an object is — a measure of how long something is — a measure of how hot an object is

2.

Weight	Distance	Capacity	Temperature
grams tonnes	centimetres inches	millilitres pints	Celsius Fahrenheit

3.

Imperial	miles, pounds, pints
Metric	centimetres, litres, kilograms

4. jug: pints and litres
ruler: centimetres and inches
thermometer: Celsius and Fahrenheit
weighing scale: pounds and kilograms

34 Length

1. (b) 100 (c) 1000
2. (a) 30 mm (b) 200 cm (c) 7000 m
3. (a) 70 mm, 70 cm, 7 m (b) 50 cm, 40 m, 40 km
4. (a) 740 cm (b) 250 cm
5. Yes, as 1.35 m is greater than 125 cm.
6. (a) kilometres, miles (b) metres, feet

35 Measuring lengths

1. (a) 26 mm (b) 50 mm (c) 41 mm (d) 73 mm
2. Use a ruler to check the lengths of all four lines.
3. About 13 m
4. About 11 m

36 Reading scales

1. (a) 24 (b) 4900
2. (a)

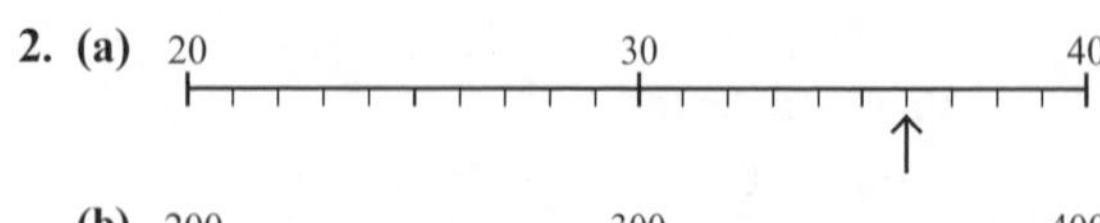

(b)

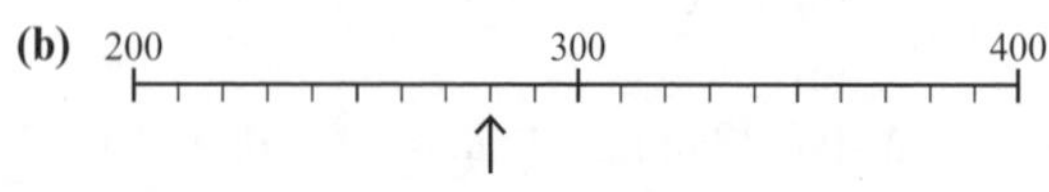

3. (a) 160 ml
(b)

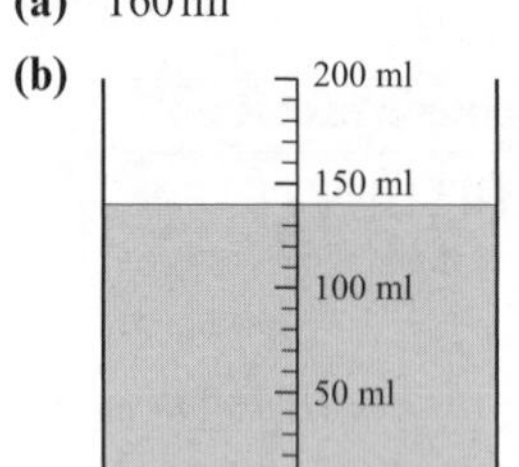

4. (a) 65 km/h (b)

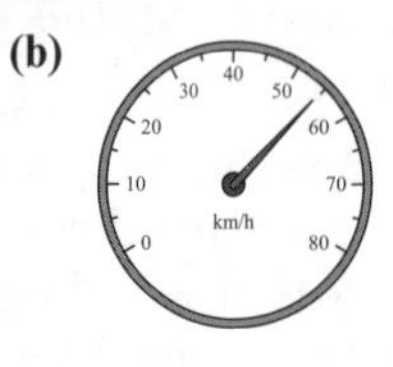

5. (a) 400 ml (b) –20 °C (c) 3.8 kg

37 Temperature

1. (a) 14 °C (b) 29 °C (c) 15 °C
2. (a) Spain (b) India (c) 7 °F
3. (a) 10 °C (b)

°C
–20 –10 0 10 20

4. 2 °C

38 Distances

1.

	Imperial	Metric
The distance between 2 towns	miles	kilometres
The distance around a small garden	feet	metres
The length of the River Thames	miles	kilometres

2. 295 miles
3. (a) 18 kilometres (b) 90 kilometres
4. (a) 18 miles (b) Amy
5. 177 feet

39 Routes

1. (a) 5.4 km (b) viewpoint
(c) viewpoint → lake → windmill
(d) lake → windmill → woodland → lake
2. (a) 20 miles
(b) home → warehouse → workshop → wholesaler
(c) scrapyard → wholesaler → workshop → warehouse → home

40 Weight

1. (a) any two of: kilograms, grams and tonnes
(b) pounds and stones
2. (a) stones or kilograms (b) tonnes (c) grams
3. 50 kg
4. 700 grams, 7 kilograms, 7 tonnes
5. 34 pounds
6. Yes, she has to pay extra as the total weight of her baggage is 16.5 kg.
7. No, as the total weight is 540 kg.
8. Eric

41 Weight calculations

1. 1000
2. (a) 6000 g (b) 8000 g
3. (a) 4700 g (b) 2850 g (c) 900 g
4. 3400 g
5. 40
6. Yes, as 5600 g is greater than 5000 g.
7. No, as 1260 g is greater than 1000 g.

42 Capacity

1. (a) Capacity (b) Volume
2. (a) 1 litre (b) 750 ml
3. (a) litres (b) millilitres (c) gallons or litres
4. 20 litres
5. 6 millilitres, 6 litres, 60 litres
6. (a) 2 pints (b) 4 litres (c) 200 ml

43 Capacity calculations

1. 1000
2. (a) 7000 ml (b) 4000 ml
3. (a) 8400 ml (b) 9750 ml
4. (a) 8 litres (b) 4350 ml
5. No, as 2660 ml is less than 3000 ml.
6. (a) 10 (b) 1600 ml

44 Money

1. (a) pounds (b) 100
2. (a) ×100 (b) ÷100
3. (a) £8.67 (b) £17.08
(c) £0.28 (d) £54.62
4. (a) 4p (b) 83p (c) 1101p

5. **(a)** 58p, 85p, £0.90, £3.58, £3.85
   (b) 32p, 320p, £32, £32.01, £32.10
6. Hair gel, as it costs less than £5

45 Money calculations

1. £1.36
2. £133
3. No, as it costs £2.16
4. Offer B
5. £6.70
6. **(a)** £0.50 **(b)** £0.30 **(c)** the large box

46 Problem-solving practice

1. by coach
2. **(a)** 450 g **(b)** 90 g
   (c)

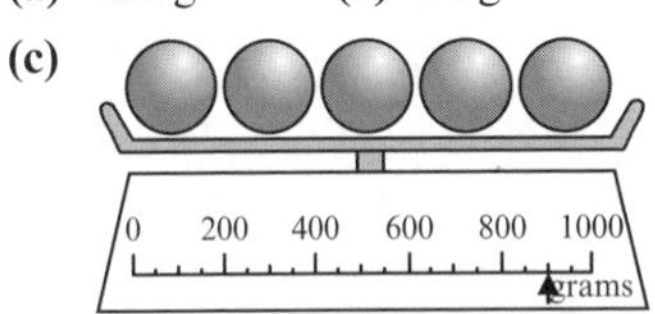

3. **(a)** 30 **(b)** £120
4. **(a)** 750 ml **(b)**

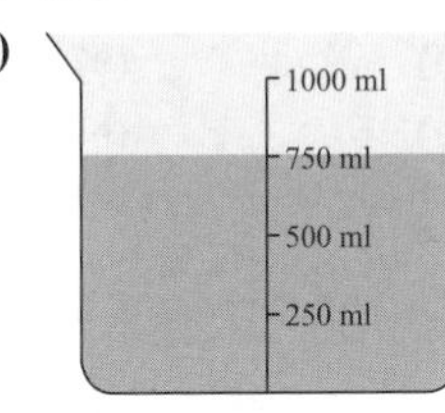

47 Problem-solving practice

1. 15
2. bowling
3. **(a)** 32 miles
   (b) home ⟶ Penn ⟶ shop ⟶ zoo
4. Shah's Grocery

SHAPE AND SPACE

48 Angles

1. A and D
2. **(a)** 4 **(b)** 2 **(c)** 1
3.

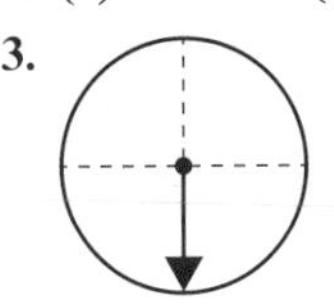

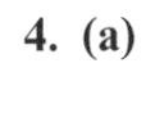

4. **(a)**

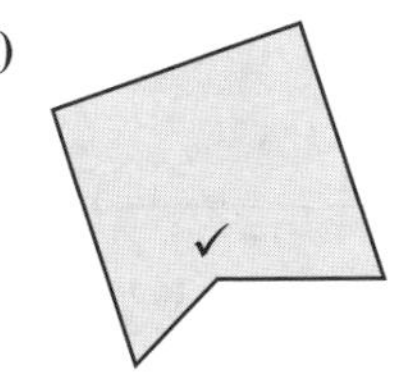

(b)

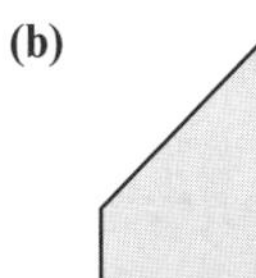

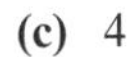

(c) 4

49 Symmetry

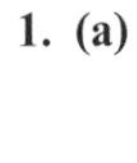

1. **(a)**

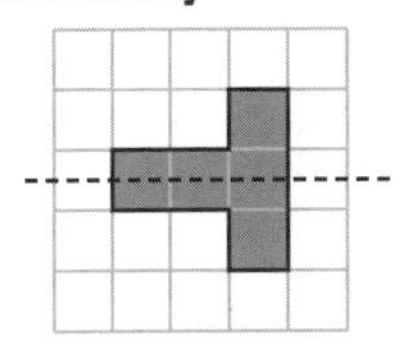

(b)

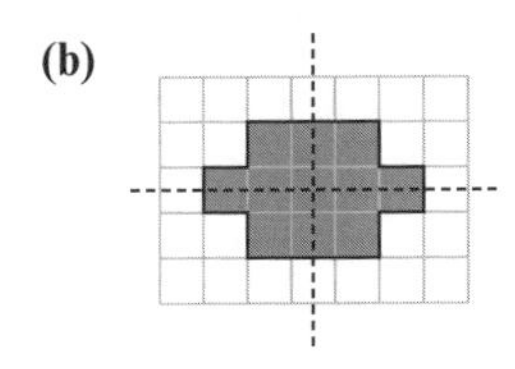

2. **(a)** There is more than one possible answer.

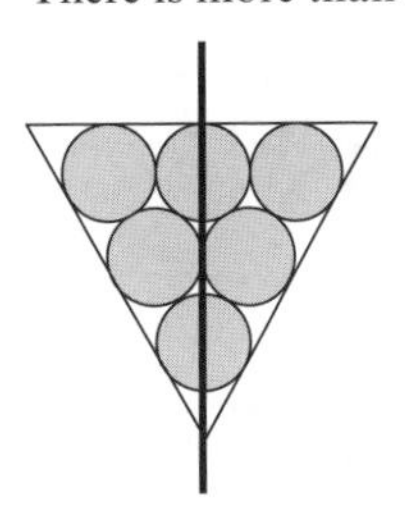

(b)

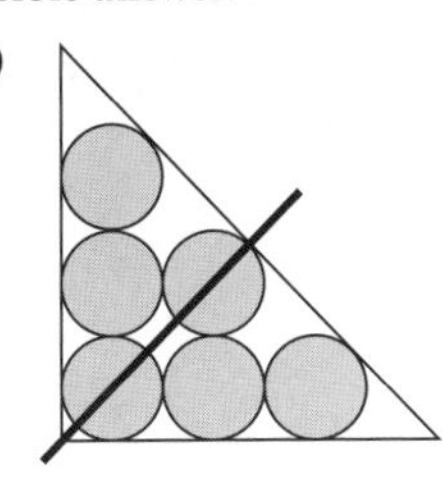

(c) There is more than one possible answer.

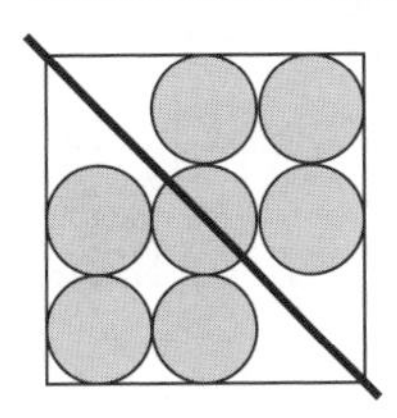

3. **(a)** A **(b)** B or C **(c)** D
4. **(a)** A, E **(b)** B, C, D

50 2D shapes

1. **(a)** equilateral triangle **(b)** rectangle
   (c) square **(d)** circle
2.

	Triangle	Square	Rectangle	Circle
Number of angles	3	4	4	0
Number of sides	3	4	4	1

3.

This shape has four straight sides and four right angles. All the sides are the same length.	square
This shape has three straight sides and three angles.	triangle
This shape has one curved side. It has no angles.	circle
This shape has four straight sides and four right angles. Two sides are long and two sides are short.	rectangle

51 3D shapes

1.

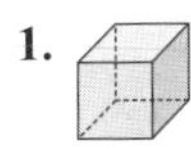

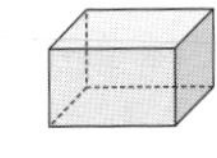

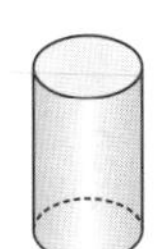

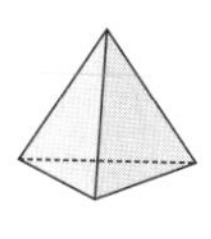

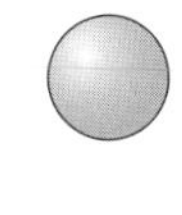

cube cuboid cylinder pyramid sphere

2.

	3D shape	Number of faces	Number of edges	Number of corners
(a)	cube	6	12	8
(b)	cuboid	6	12	8
(c)	square-based pyramid	5	8	5
(d)	tetrahedron	4	6	4
(e)	triangular prism	5	9	6

3. **(a)** 10 **(b)** 24 **(c)** 16

52 Using plans

1. (a) rectangle (b) 8

(c)

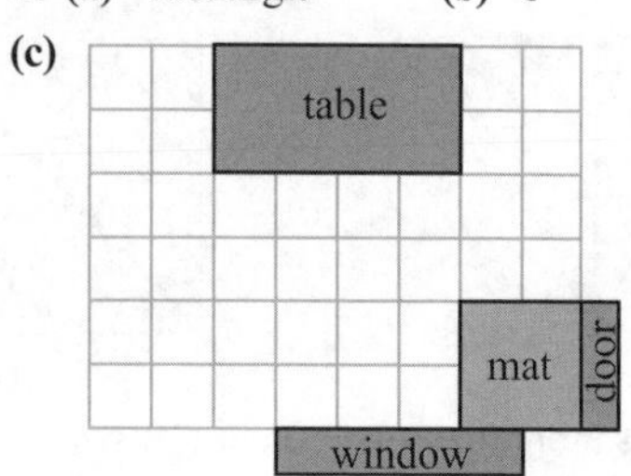

2. (a) square

(b) For example:

flowerbed
pond
greenhouse

3. Block 1 row B

53 Problem-solving practice

1.

	A	B	C
Name of shape	rectangle	square	circle
Number of right angles	4	4	0

2. (a) cuboid (b) (i) 6 (ii) 12 (iii) 8

3. (a) B (b) C
(c) A (d) A

54 Problem-solving practice

1. cylinder, cone, cube

2. shape 4

3. For example:

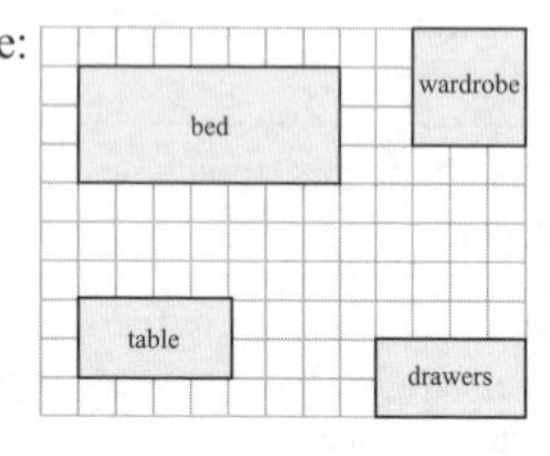

HANDLING DATA

55 Lists

1. £20.30

2. No, she should get £1.65 change.

3. £61.50

4. Akaal Limited

56 Tables

1. (a) £5.90 (b) £5.60
(c) It is more expensive to rent a speedboat in September than to rent a kayak in June.

2. (a) 35 (b) 33 (c) 80

3. £166.50

57 Tally charts

1 (a)

Display	animals	traction engines	fruit and veg	country crafts
Tally	卌	卌 卌	卌 I	卌 卌 II
Frequency	5	10	6	12

(b) 10 (c) 33

2 (a)

Preferred activity	rafting	sewing	climbing	hiking
Tally	卌 III	I	卌 II	IIII
Frequency	8	1	7	4

(b) rafting (c) 4

3. (a)

Type of film	Tally	Frequency
horror	IIII	4
documentary	III	3
comedy	卌 II	7
romance	卌 卌 II	12

(b) documentary (c) 4 (d) 26

58 Reading bar charts

1. (a) wood (b) 10 (c) 10

2. (a) 10 (b) desktop computer
(c) 3 (d) 27

59 Completing a bar chart

1.

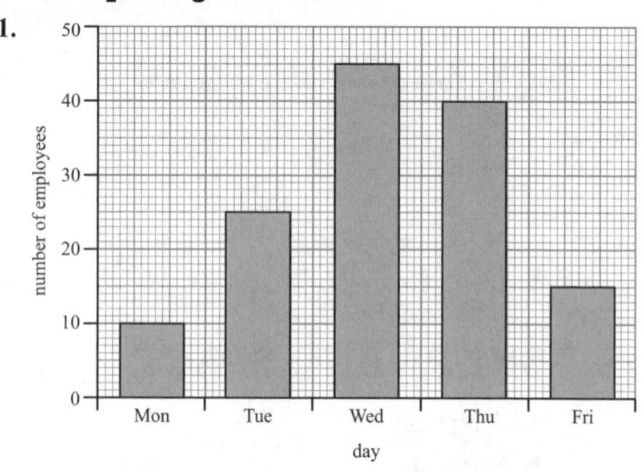

2.

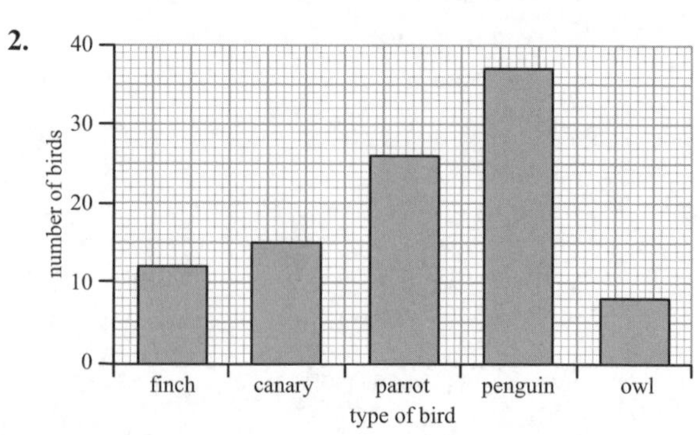

60 Reading pictograms

1. (a) 40 (b) 10 (c) Thursday and Friday

2. (a) Vegworld (b) 2 (c) 8

61 Reading pie charts

1. (a) sparrow (b) $\frac{1}{4}$ (c) 16

2. (a) posters (b) $\frac{1}{3}$ (c) 24

62 Problem-solving practice

1. (a)

Type of sandwich	Tally	Frequency
ham and tomato	卌 卌 卌 卌 II	22
egg and cheese	卌 卌 卌 III	18
cheese and pickle	卌 IIII	9
tuna and mayonnaise	卌 卌 I	11

   (b) 40 (c) 60

2. Heptathlon

3.

	Tea	Coffee	Milkshakes
Saturday	65	50	40
Sunday	70	45	25

63 Problem-solving practice

1. (a) 36 (b) 27 (c) 15 (d) 150

2. (a)

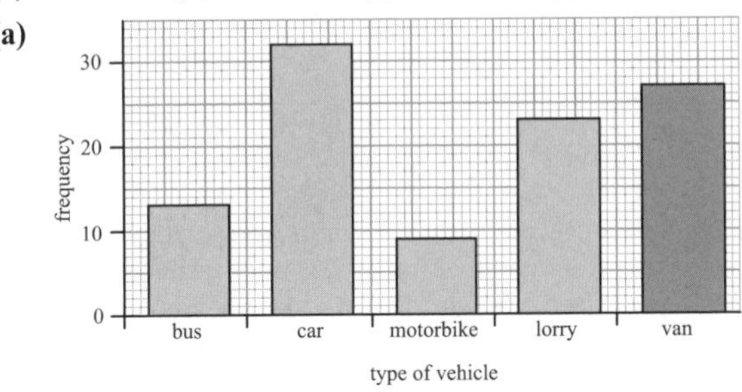

   (b) van (c) 104

PRACTICE PAPER

64 Planning a concert

1. (a) 400 (b) 8 (c) (8 × 25) + 50 = £250

66 At the concert

2. (a) 3 × 60p = £1.80 which is greater than £1.50 so it is cheaper to buy a pack of three bottles.
   (b) 72 (c) 60 (d) 60 × 3 = 180
   (e) cuboid
   (f) Magic Man, Comedy, Animation, DJ Fun

69 On the way home

3. (a) concert hall ⟶ Himley ⟶ home (13 miles)
   (b) 8 hours

70 Finances

4. (a) adults (b) 300 + 200 + 140 + 180 = £820

Published by Pearson Education Limited, 80 Strand, London, WC2R 0RL.

www.pearsonschoolsandfecolleges.co.uk

Copies of official specifications for all Edexcel qualifications may be found on the website: www.edexcel.com

Edited, typeset and produced by Elektra Media Ltd

Illustrated by Elektra Media Ltd
Cover illustration by Miriam Sturdee

First published 2017

20 19 18 17
10 9 8 7 6 5 4 3 2 1

British Library Cataloguing in Publication Data
A catalogue record for this book is available from the British Library

ISBN 978 1 292 14560 0

Printed in Slovakia by Neografia